June 2007

To Gordon,

Thank you for facilitating my

learning in history.

With my best wishes,

Francis

CHIROPRACTIC
IN EUROPE
AN ILLUSTRATED HISTORY

CHIROPRACTIC
IN EUROPE

AN ILLUSTRATED HISTORY

Edited by

Francis J. H. Wilson

Matador
9 De Montfort Mews
Leicester LE1 7FW, UK
Tel: (+44) 116 255 9311 / 9312
Email: books@troubador.co.uk
Web: www.troubador.co.uk/matador

ISBN 13: 978-1-905886-869

Typeset in 11pt Bembo by Troubador Publishing Ltd, Leicester, UK

Matador is an imprint of Troubador Publishing Ltd

In memory of Kyrre Myhrvold, chiropractor, President of the Norwegian Chiropractors' Association 1986 to 1994, chiropractic historian

"A profession without a written history is a spineless profession. Pride and identity in one's profession is based on knowledge of the past and goals for the future."
Kyrre Myhrvold, 1998

CONTENTS

SECTION B
HISTORIES OF CHIROPRACTIC IN EUROPEAN NATIONS

PREFACE

In May 1997, at a General Council Meeting of the European Chiropractors' Union (ECU), it was unanimously agreed that a written history of chiropractic in Europe should be produced. The initial co-ordinator of the project was Kyrre Myhrvold, a chiropractor from Norway. Unfortunately, Dr Myhrvold's commitments were such that he was unable to see the project through to completion and I took over from him as co-ordinator of the work in 2000. Sadly, in October 2003, Dr Myhrvold passed away, at the age of 57. This book is dedicated to his memory.

Chiropractic has existed in Europe for 100 years. For 75 of those years the European Chiropractors' Union has represented the profession in Europe at supra-national level. This history was commissioned by the ECU and focuses primarily on nations and bodies associated with the ECU. The book is divided into 2 sections. The first part of the book provides an overview of chiropractic's history from a European perspective. In the second part of the book, the histories of chiropractic in 19 European nations are examined.

Most of the contributors to the volume are not professional historians but chiropractors, individuals who have been deeply involved in the recent development of the profession in Europe, individuals with significant insight and relevant knowledge. For many of them English is a second language. That being the case, I feel humbled by the quality of work produced.

For those new to the field, I hope that this book will provide a valuable introduction to chiropractic's history from a European perspective. For those already familiar with chiropractic's history, I hope that the book will add to your understanding and increase your interest in the subject.

Francis Wilson, January 2007

FOREWORD

I am very proud to introduce this History of chiropractic in Europe. It has been a long journey gathering together information from all over the Old Continent.

Francis Wilson, the editor, in conjunction with the other authors, has strived to give a true picture of the profession, and has collected many photographs and documents, some of which have never been publicly seen before. When you read it, you feel the maturity of the European chiropractic profession developing through the years, culminating in its adult phase!

Fantastic work to celebrate the 75th anniversary of ECU! Thank you Francis. Thank you to everyone involved in producing this book.

Philippe Druart
ECU President, January 2007

CONTRIBUTORS

Tuomo Ahola, DC, BSc, BA
Practising chiropractor, Orivesi, Finland

Bengt Axén, DC
Practising chiropractor, Vällingby, Sweden

Søren Bak-Jensen, MA, PhD
Senior Curator, Medical Museion, University
of Copenhagen, Denmark

Ben Bolsenbroek, BSc, DC
Practising chiropractor, Haarlem, the
Netherlands

Andrew Doody, DC
Practising chiropractor, Stillorgan, Ireland

John Gillet, DC
Practising chiropractor, Brussels, Belgium

Vasileios Gkolfinopoulos, BSc, MSc, DC
Practising chiropractor, Athens, Greece

Ann Hagéus, DC
Chiropractor (non-practising), Sweden

Jeff Heese, DC, BA
Practising chiropractor, Madrid, Spain

Tryggvi Jónasson, DC
Practising chiropractor, Reykjavík, Iceland

Joseph Keating Jr, PhD, Litt D (hon)
Professor, Cleveland Chiropractic College,
Kansas City, USA

Beatrice Mikus, DC
Chiropractor (non-practising), Liechtenstein

Christopher Mikus, DC
Practising chiropractor, Schaan, Liechtenstein

Daniel Mühlemann, PT, DC
Practising chiropractor, Zürich, Switzerland

John Naef, DC
Practising chiropractor, Zürich, Switzerland

Øystein Ogre, DC
Practising chiropractor, Fredrikstad, Norway

Efstathios (Stathis) Papadopoulos, DC
Practising chiropractor, Lefcosia, Cyprus

Thomas Rigel, DC
Practising chiropractor, Rome, Italy

Benoit Rouy, DC
Practising chiropractor, Auxerre, France

Edward Saltys, DC
Practising chiropractor, Lagoa, Portugal

Louis Stephany, DC
Practising chiropractor, Oberfeulen,
Luxembourg

Ingrid White, BS, DC
Practising chiropractor, Kaiserslautern,
Germany

Francis Wilson, DC, MSc
Senior Lecturer, Anglo-European College of
Chiropractic, Bournemouth, England

ACKNOWLEDGEMENTS

The Editor is grateful to the many people who have given of their time and expertise to make this book a reality. It has been a collective effort, not only on the part of the authors, to whom I am particularly indebted, but also on the part of many individuals and organisations who have worked behind the scenes to produce it. It is not possible to acknowledge everyone here, but I am appreciative of all the help and support that has been received.

Special thanks are due to Philippe Druart, President of the European Chiropractors' Union (ECU), to Anne Kemp, Executive Secretary of the ECU, to Jean Robert, Academic Dean of the new European Academy of Chiropractic, and to the members of the Executive Administrative Council of the ECU. I would also like to acknowledge the assistance received from the chiropractic associations of Europe, from ProChiropractic Europe, and from the chiropractors of Europe.

This work would not have been possible without the backing of Ken Vall, Principal of the Anglo-European College of Chiropractic (AECC), and the support of colleagues, faculty and staff, at the College. I would also like to thank those of other universities, schools and libraries, who have supported this venture. In relation to my collaborative work with Joseph Keating for the first section of this book, I would like to acknowledge support from Cleveland Chiropractic College and the National Institute of Chiropractic Research. For facilitating my learning in history, Jenni Bolton of the AECC, Bernard Harris and Gordon Causer of the University of Southampton, deserve special mention. To the publishers of this book, Jeremy Thompson and his team at Troubador, my sincere thanks.

Finally, I would like to thank my family, especially my wife Rachel, who has read and re-read the text in order to remove errors, and who has made many sacrifices in order that this work might be completed.

Francis Wilson, January 2007

SECTION A

AN OVERVIEW OF THE HISTORY OF CHIROPRACTIC FROM A EUROPEAN PERSPECTIVE

Francis JH Wilson and Joseph C Keating Jr

PART 1

Before the European Chiropractic Union: origins, early development and context of chiropractic

1. Origins of chiropractic in the United States

Chiropractic began in Davenport, Iowa, a city on the western bank of the Mississippi River in the Midwest of the United States, approximately 150 miles west of Chicago. In the 1880s Davenport was part of an expanding metropolitan area, one of the Tri-Cities, the others being Rock Island and Moline[1].

Figure 1. Daniel David Palmer, as schoolmaster in Louisa, Iowa, circa 1870

Daniel David Palmer, the founder of chiropractic, moved to Davenport in the late 1880s. He was born in Canada, in Pickering, Ontario, just east of Toronto on 7th March 1845[2]. His family relocated to Port Perry, Ontario, in about 1860. With the influx of draft dodgers during the American Civil War (1861-1865), the labour market in the Canadian province became flooded and the family moved again, this time to the heartland of the United States. DD, as he has become affectionately known, worked as a schoolteacher, cultivated a nursery, kept bees, and ran a grocery store. His journal suggests that his beekeeping venture came to an end in 1881 following a particularly cold winter. His record for 14th April 1881 reads simply: "Bees all dead"[3].

Figure 2. Jacob S Caster, magnetic healer
"This is a man whom everyone knows, out of whose fingers a live current flows"

(From a portfolio of cartoons published by the Burlington Hawkeye Newspaper, 1913)

Despite limited formal education, DD's voracious appetite for books served him well. He matured in an age of machines, the industrial revolution of the United States. The culture of the time was full of the wonders that emerging science and technology offered: steamboats, railroads, telegraphy, electric lights, moving pictures, and by the early years of the twentieth century – flying machines!

People were open to new ideas, and a variety of novel theories and philosophies abounded. Among these were phrenology, which suggested that human behaviour could be predicted, perhaps even controlled; spiritualism, the notion that it was possible to communicate with the dead, an idea that had grown popular as Americans yearned for loved ones who had died in the Civil War; theosophy, which offered a vision that the laws of nature and the laws of the spirit were but reflections of one another; and homeopathy, herbalism and eclectic medicine, which offered gentler alternatives to the harsh remedies of mainstream, *heroic* medicine, such as blood letting and administration of highly toxic drugs.

Magnetic healing, imported from Europe and based upon theories introduced by the Austrian physician Franz Anton Mesmer, offered yet another alternative to the medical orthodoxy of the day. The idea that *vital energy* could be passed from clinician to patient, thereby overcoming disease and restoring health, captured Palmer's imagination. An entry in his day book suggests that he saw his first patient as a magnetic healer on Friday 3rd September 1886 in Burlington, Iowa[4]. His name appears in the Burlington City Directory of 1887 under physicians: magnetic[5]. Classified with him under physicians were allopathic, oculist, botanic, eclectic and homeopathic practitioners. Also in Burlington at the time was one Jacob Caster (son of Paul Caster), a second generation magnetic healer[6]. It is possible that this man, who later became Mayor of Burlington, influenced Palmer. Ironically, Jacob Caster's son Charles would study chiropractic a quarter of a century later[7].

Palmer did not stay long in Burlington. He soon moved up the Mississippi River to Davenport where he established another magnetic healing practice. There chiropractic was born. DD's first chiropractic patient, a janitor in the building where Palmer conducted his practice, authored the first published account of chiropractic healing:

Figure 3. Harvey Lillard, DD Palmer's first chiropractic patient

(From Palmer BJ. In: *The Science of Chiropractic. Illustration no. 29. Davenport: The Palmer School of Chiropractic; 1906*)

"I was deaf 17 years and I expected to always remain so, for I had doctored a great deal without any benefit. I had long ago made up my mind to not take any more ear treatments, for it did me no good.

Last January Dr. Palmer told me that my deafness came from an injury in my spine. This was new to me; but it is a fact that my back was injured at the time I went deaf. Dr. Palmer treated me on the spine; in two treatments I could hear quite well. That was eight months ago. My hearing remains good."[8]

Palmer later described the origin of his new discipline in, *The Chiropractor's Adjustor: The*

Science, Art and Philosophy of Chiropractic, published in 1910:

"I was a magnetic healer for nine years previous to discovering the principles which comprise the method known as chiropractic. During this period much of that which was necessary to complete the science was worked out. I had discovered that many diseases were associated with derangements of the stomach, kidneys and other organs …

One question was always uppermost in my mind in my search for the cause of disease. I desired to know why one person was ailing and his associate, eating at the same table, working in the same shop, at the same bench, was not. **Why?** What difference was there in the two persons that caused one to have pneumonia, catarrh, typhoid or rheumatism, while his partner, similarly situated, escaped! **Why?** This question had worried thousands for centuries and was answered in September 1895 …

Figure 4. Palmer's Chiropractic Cure and Infirmary, Davenport, was located on the third floor of the Putnam Building in the Ryan Block, image circa 1900

(Courtesy of Leonard Vernon, DC)

Harvey Lillard a janitor in the Ryan Block, where I had my office, had been so deaf for 17 years that he could not hear the racket of a wagon on the street or the ticking of a watch. I made inquiry as to the cause of his deafness and was informed that when he was exerting himself in a cramped, stooping position, he felt something give way in his back and immediately became deaf. An examination showed a vertebra racked from its normal position. I reasoned that if that vertebra was replaced, the man's hearing should be restored. With this object in view, a half-hour's talk persuaded Mr. Lillard to allow me to replace it. I racked it into position by using the spinous process as a lever and soon the man could hear as before. There was nothing "accidental" about this, as it was accomplished with an object in view, and the result expected was obtained. There was nothing "crude" about this adjustment; it was specific, so much so that no Chiropractor has equalled it …

Shortly after this relief of deafness, I had a case of heart trouble which was not improving. I examined the spine and found a displaced vertebra pressing against the nerves which innervate the heart. I adjusted the vertebra and gave immediate relief – nothing "accidental" or "crude" about this. Then I began to reason if two diseases, so dissimilar as deafness and heart trouble, came from impingement, a pressure on nerves, were not other diseases due to a similar cause?"[9]

Palmer's initial theory of chiropractic, a derivative of his quest to understand the benefits he believed his patients had derived from his magnetic practice, construed inflammation as the essential quality of disease. He believed that inflammation arose from the heat of friction generated by anatomic parts out of their normal position. He believed that he could effect a re-positioning, and thereby relieve and/or prevent inflammation and disease, through the use of manipulation or *adjusting*[10-12]. During this period Palmer used mechanical metaphors, such as likening the human body to a machine. Later, he would re-interpret his chiropractic experiences in light of the supernatural beliefs that had originally guided his magnetic practice. He would become a born-again vitalist, emphasising a belief that life was dependent on a force distinct from the purely physical or chemical. Palmer believed that this intellectual force, which he described as *Innate Intelligence*, expressed itself through the human nervous system. He thought that if Innate Intelligence was able to communicate with all parts of the human body, through the nervous system, then the patient would be healthy. If there were obstructions to flow of *mental impulses*, due to *subluxation* (mal-position of joints), especially, but not exclusively those of the spine, disease would develop. Displaced vertebrae, he hypothesised, could cause impingement of nerves and compromise the expression of Innate. Palmer's chiropractic would concern itself with the identification and correction of bony misalignments in order to promote health. The name *chiropractic* was derived from Greek words offered by Reverend Samuel Weed, one of Palmer's patients[13].

Palmer's chiropractic shared much in common with Andrew Taylor Still's osteopathy, which pre-dated chiropractic. In his autobiography, Still tells us that it was on the 22nd June 1874 that he "flung to the breeze the banner of Osteopathy"[14]. By 1892 he had opened a school of osteopathy in Kirksville, Missouri, south of Davenport[15]. Both Still and Palmer advocated the use of manipulation to restore bodily alignment and to remove mechanical obstructions that they believed would otherwise tend to compromise systems of communication within the body. Although there has been no conclusive evidence published to show that Palmer visited Still in Kirksville in the years before or after the birth of chiropractic, and Palmer adamantly denied such a visit, he readily acknowledged that osteopathy was one of several methods of healing that he had studied:

> "I have taken lessons and studied Christian Science, Faith Cure, Mind Cure, Metaphysics, Magnetic and Osteopathy, therefore I am acquainted with each and know their differences. Any of them are better than drugging. A person who has not studied them is not capable of judging their curative effects."[16]

Clearly Palmer did not develop his ideas in a vacuum, and there were those in the osteopathic community who believed Palmer

Figure 5. Andrew Taylor Still, founder of osteopathy

had taken Still's ideas and passed them off as his own. Such was not the case. Still employed manipulation to keep open the channels (nerves and circulation) from brain to end-organ, so as to maintain health and restore it when lost. Palmer's early chiropractic method sought to relieve inflammation by repositioning any displaced anatomical part which might be causing friction. His theory posited that friction gave rise to heat which caused tissues to inflame and malfunction. On the technical side, Palmer did not claim to be the first person to advocate spinal manipulation. He did claim, however, to be the first to replace displaced vertebrae using the spinous and transverse processes as levers, and he did claim chiropractic to be a distinct system[17-18].

2. Early development of chiropractic in the United States

Palmer established a successful business in Davenport. HJ Parker, who worked as a bookkeeper in the Ryan Block where Palmer rented rooms, wrote of him:

> "Eight years ago Dr. Palmer came here and rented three rooms. We then thought him a humbug, and that it would only be a short time till his rooms would be vacant and he departed; but instead we have been happily surprised to see his practice steadily increase, until he is now occupying 42 rooms for his business and the accommodation of patients who come

from a distance. Generally it is only a short time until they are able to depart with health restored. I have seen patients that would have to crawl up the stairway to his rooms, and others carried there, who would in a very short time go away seemingly restored to perfect health."[19]

DD Palmer had advertised to solicit students even before the birth of chiropractic. The January 1897 issue of his flyer, *The Chiropractic*, reveals his switch from teaching magnetic healing to teaching chiropractic at Palmer's School of Magnetic Cure, which he had incorporated in the summer of 1896. J LeRoy Baker was the first student to study chiropractic under Palmer[20]. In the years that followed others came to study the new discipline, initially by means of an apprenticeship. In 1902, Bartlett Joshua Palmer, DD Palmer's son, received his chiropractic diploma from his father.

Whereas the last years of the nineteenth century were a time of success for DD Palmer, the first years of the twentieth century were less so. Following a period of growth in the practice at Davenport a series of misfortunes befell him. One of his students, a man named Reiring, raised concerns about the quality of instruction given by Palmer and a legal battle ensued[21]. It appears that at about this time business slowed and Palmer fell into debt[22]. To make matters worse, medical licensing laws began to be enforced in Iowa[23]. Palmer was not licensed. Daniel David Palmer left Davenport in or about 1902 in order to search

Figure 6. Daniel David Palmer, chiropractor, circa 1906
"I give such balms as have no strife
With nature or the laws of life;
With blood my hands I never stain,
Nor poison men to ease their pain."

(Palmer's motto from The Chiropractic 1897; January (17), 2)

for a friend and colleague, Thomas Storey, who had gone missing[24]. His son took over running the business at Davenport. From this point onwards Bartlett Joshua Palmer moved to centre stage in the chiropractic story.

Despite his young age, he was 20 at the time, his limited experience as a chiropractor, and the threat of prosecution, BJ Palmer set about developing the practice and school. In this he almost certainly received financial support from Howard Nutting[25]. Even taking this into account, it is testament to the character of BJ Palmer that despite the challenges he faced, the school flourished.

In the years that followed the Palmer School became a thriving institution. Recognising the power of effective advertising, and having

Figure 7. Bartlett Joshua Palmer, developer of chiropractic, circa 1902

taken full control of the School from his father in 1906, BJ Palmer initiated a series of marketing activities. He installed a printing house at the School, a phonographic department, and by 1922 there was even a radio station, *Wonders of Chiropractic* (WOC)[26]. Lasting legacies of this time are the first of a series of *Green Books* produced at the Palmer School. These books were so named because of their dark green covers. The first, *The Science of Chiropractic*, compiled by BJ Palmer, but based on his father's work, was published in 1906[27].

Word of chiropractic spread across the United States with phenomenal speed. New schools sprung up in competition to the Palmer School of Chiropractic at Davenport. One of the first was the Chiropractic Cure and School, which became the American School of Chiropractic and Nature Cure, established in Cedar Rapids[28-29]. This School was the brainchild of Solon M Langworthy, Oakley G Smith and Minora C Paxton, former students of DD Palmer. Langworthy moved to Cedar Rapids after completing studies under Palmer in 1901, but considered the principles of chiropractic within a wider context of *nature cure*, encouraging integration of chiropractic, osteopathic and naturopathic approaches. Between 1900 and 1925 more than 80 chiropractic schools came to exist in North America, offering courses of varying type, length and quality[30-31]. Whilst BJ Palmer took control in Davenport, DD Palmer established schools in other parts of the country.

Figure 8. The campus of the Palmer School of Chiropractic, as it was in the early 1920s

The first quarter of the twentieth century saw prolific growth of chiropractic in North America, but this growth was met with resistance, not least of which came from the medical mainstream and laws that supported powers and privileges of the medical fraternity. Many chiropractors in the United States were indicted for practising medicine without a licence[32-33]. Many served prison sentences, DD Palmer among them. The resistance that chiropractors faced during this period was a factor which led to increased organisation within the occupation in order that it might defend itself effectively. It was during these years that the first national associations of chiropractors, the American Chiropractic Association, affiliated with the American School of Chiropractic, and the Universal Chiropractors' Association, affiliated with the Palmer School of Chiropractic, came into being[34].

In 1913 chiropractic's founder died, but chiropractic lived on in the hands of a growing number of individuals who chose to make chiropractic their career. Increasingly, prospective students would travel not only from within North America to study chiropractic, but from across the globe.

3. European pioneers

By 1905 news of chiropractic had reached Europe. On 28th March 1905 Elizabeth Van Raders wrote to DD Palmer from Nice, France:

"Dear Sir – Enclosed find 50 cents for a year's subscription to The Chiropractor. I thank you very much for your literature. I have read it with much interest, and think it simply marvelous (sic), so much so, that I am longing to be in Davenport, so as to become a Chiropractor.

I have talked about it to my Magnetic Doctor. He is so much interested, that I am now translating your article "Luxation of bones cause disease," and shall translate others into the French language. He believes you are a great magnetizer."[35]

In 1906 Elizabeth Van Raders made the journey from France to the United States to study at the Palmer School of Chiropractic (PSC)[36]. In the same year 3 other Europeans attended the School: Godfrey PM Heathcote from England, Marie S Nesseth from Norway, and C Rasmussen, also from Norway[37]. These individuals were the first Europeans known to have studied chiropractic. It is not clear how Marie Nesseth and C Rasmussen came to be in Davenport in 1906, but the following is Godfrey Heathcote's story as reported in the Journal of the Palmer School of Chiropractic, *The Chiropractor.*

Figure 9. Class group from the Palmer School of Chiropractic, circa 1906, including GPM Heathcote (England), MS Nesseth (Norway), C Rasmussen (Norway) and E Van Raders (France)

(From Palmer BJ. In: The Science of Chiropractic. Illustration no. 25. Davenport: The Palmer School of Chiropractic; 1906)

"This important event was brought about quite by accident, as I had never heard of Chiropractic before the earthquake in San Francisco. I had intended to spend the summer in Santa Cruz, assisting Miss Hanly, professional nurse and masseuse, who owned a twenty room sanitarium there. Miss Hanly at that time received some of *The P.S.C.* Chiropractic literature, which interested me very much. I determined to go east to study, there being no business in California owing to the earthquake. I started for Davenport and *The P.S.C.*, where I considered that I

Figure 10. Palmer School of Chiropractic, parade, 1913. Note the European flags in the procession.

would obtain the best education in Anatomy and Neurology, two branches I always considered to be the most important in the human body. Since my arrival, having taken adjustments, have felt much better, my nerves being very much shattered by the effects of the earthquake, as I had a narrow escape for my life, a brick chimney falling on my bed and cutting my shoulder. I look upon my investment for the nine months' course in Chiropractic, as the best I have made since my arrival in the United States fourteen years ago."[38]

Letters from Paris, France and from Devonshire, England, were published in the December 1906 – January 1907 edition of *The Chiropractor*. These came from Elizabeth Van

Raders and Godfrey Heathcote respectively. Chiropractic had arrived in Europe. Elizabeth Van Raders wrote to BJ Palmer in relation to his book, *The Science of Chiropractic*:

> "The general makeup of the book is very artistic and in conformity with its high mission. In order to introduce Chiropractic successfully to the European Scientific world it will be necessary to arrange a special edition that will be confined to a strictly scientific dissertation on the principles and philosophy of chiropractic."[39]

It would not be long before both Van Raders and Heathcote would return to the United States. In June 1907 Elizabeth Van Raders, now using the post-nominal letters DC,

Figure 11. Faculty at the Palmer School of Chiropractic, 1918

Doctor of Chiropractic, wrote to the Palmer School from Berkeley, California[40]. In 1908 Godfrey Heathcote, DC, was listed as a member of the newly formed Universal Chiropractors' Association, resident in Los Angeles, California[41].

Only a handful of chiropractors came to Europe in the years before the First World War, and it was not until some time after the Great War that chiropractors arrived in Europe in significant numbers and began to organise themselves. It has been claimed that during the War chiropractors drafted into the US military came to fight in Europe and provided chiropractic treatments in the trenches[42]. There is evidence to suggest that this was indeed the case. In January 1919 a letter from Mart Callahan, a graduate of the National School of Chiropractic, was published in the *National Journal of Chiropractic*:

"I had one case of shell shock thus far. Both arms of the patient were affected, but after six adjustments I succeeded in removing the tremor from the left arm. He was then sent home, so I did not get a real chance to see what I could do, but am sure that we can do more than the M.D.'s in such cases. Boy, go to it!

I am on the staff in the Orthopedic Ward as masseur, and have charge of all the manipulative and reconstructive work. I have had fine luck so far and like the work very much. The captain under whom I work is a good man on Orthopedics and a prince to work for. He also comes from Rochester, so I hope to get some business from him when I return to practice. By the way, I have a prospective student here who works for me. Her name is Miss Lavers and she is from somewhere in New Jersey, so please send me a copy of our prospectus, as I don't know her very well, and I'll do the rest..."[43]

4. European context: medicine, bonesetting and osteopathy

Before the arrival of the first chiropractors to Europe, the medical profession had established itself as the primary provider of healthcare services for the European peoples. Despite dominance of the medical profession, there also existed many drugless healthcare practitioners, and amongst these were manual therapists (individuals who gave treatment by hand): bonesetters, masseuses and their like.

For generations European bonesetters had managed joint problems and set broken bones, with the necessary knowledge and skills being passed down through families by oral tradition. In France a bonesetter was called a *rebouteux*, in Germany a *knocheneinrichter*, and in Spain an *algebrista*. In Denmark bonesetting was practised by traditional healers known as *kloge folk*[44]. On the whole, bonesetting was associated with the lower classes and was not generally well regarded by those of high social standing, although a few bonesetters became widely known, even famous. In the eighteenth century one such bonesetter was Mrs Sarah Mapp of Epsom, England, who in 1736 found herself the subject of the following verses:

> "You surgeons of London, who puzzle your pates, to ride in your coaches and purchase estates, give over, for shame, for your pride has a fall, and the doctress of Epsom has outdone you all.
>
> What signifies learning, or going to school, when a woman can do, without reason or rule, what puts you to nonplus, and baffles your art; for petticoat-practice has now got the start.
>
> Dame nature has giv'n her a doctor's degree, she gets all the patients, and pockets the fee; so if you don't instantly prove her a cheat, she'll loll in her chariot whilst you walk the street."[45]

Figure 12. Caricature, thought to be of Sarah Mapp, bonesetter, who rose to fame in eighteenth century England

(From an etching by G Cruikshank, 1819. Original image from W Hogarth's 'The Company of Undertakers' (1736))

The nature of bonesetting was such that little was written about it by the bonesetters themselves. A short text on the subject was published by Thomas Moulton in the seventeenth century entitled *The Compleat Bonesetter*[46], but it was not until the second half of the nineteenth century, when a number of medical authors took an interest in bonesetting, that a series of books and papers about it were published in the English language. In 1867 James Paget delivered a lecture at St Bartholomew's Hospital, London, the content of which was published in the *British Medical Journal*[47]. It called upon doctors to "Learn to imitate what is good and avoid what is bad in the practice of bone-setters". In 1871 Wharton Hood wrote a series of articles about bonesetting, which were first published in the *Lancet*, and then republished in the form of a book[48-52]. In 1884 George Matthews Bennett published, *The Art of the Bone-setter: a Testimony and a Vindication*[53]. Together these publications, and publications which followed them, raised the profile of bonesetting, bringing the names of bonesetters like Regina Dal Cin, an Austrian born bonesetter who practised mainly in Italy, and Herbert Atkinson Barker and Richard Hutton, Englishmen, to the attention of a wider audience. When chiropractic first arrived in Europe, it seems likely that many European medical doctors would have been broadly familiar with the manipulative therapies of bonesetters. If this was the case, it is also likely that an association would have been drawn between use of manipulation and folk practitioners lacking in formal education.

Chiropractic first arrived in Europe from the United States in the first decade of the twentieth century, but was preceded by osteopathy. In 1903 the osteopath John Martin Littlejohn visited hospitals in Austria, France and Germany, having already introduced osteopathy to Britain in 1898[54]. By the end of World War I formal osteopathic training existed in Europe, following the incorporation of the British School of Osteopathy in 1917.

In their therapeutic approach, the first osteopaths and chiropractors to practise in

Figure 13. Manipulation of the knee, from an article by the medical doctor Wharton Hood, published in the Lancet in April 1871

(From Hood W. On the so-called "bone-setting", its nature and results (continued). Lancet 1871; 97 (2485), 499-501)

Europe shared with bonesetters an emphasis on manipulation. The following passage, which was written about bonesetting in 1871, might have been written about chiropractic or osteopathy in the early twentieth century:

"It is known to most practitioners of surgery, and has been known to many to their great cost and loss, that a large proportion of the cases of impaired mobility or usefulness of limbs after injury fall into the hands of a class of men called "bone-setters". In all these cases it is the custom of such men to say that the affected bone or joint is "out", although there may be an entire absence of the anatomical signs of displacement; and they proceed in due course to the performance of manipulations by which, in many instances, the patient is speedily cured."[48]

5. Initial organisation of chiropractic in Europe

After the end of the First World War, a number of chiropractors travelled from the United States to set up practice in Europe, and a number of Europeans travelled to the United States to study chiropractic. By 1923, 5 years after the cessation of hostilities, chiropractic had spread, if thinly, to at least 10 European nations: Belgium, Denmark, France, Italy, the Netherlands, Norway, Spain, Sweden, Switzerland and the United Kingdom. Chiropractic was establishing itself in Europe.

At this time very few Europeans would have heard of chiropractic. The distinction between chiropractic and the related disciplines of bonesetting and osteopathy would have been clear to even fewer. In 1926 J Henry Jones published what was possibly the first European book about chiropractic, but its title, *Healing by Manipulation (Bone-setting)*, did not effectively allude to its content. It might be assumed that one reason why the word chiropractic did not appear in the title was that few of the intended audience would have heard of it. In the forward of the book Jones wrote:

"There exist to-day schools of healing which hold aloof from drugs, and which cure disease by adjusting the bones…In England these new practitioners frequently work as isolated units, without any efficient organisation; in America they are very powerfully organised, and have received official recognition. In England they often call themselves manipulators, bone-setters, or by some similar name, though latterly the words "chiropractor" and "osteopath" have been increasingly used."[55]

In truth, chiropractors had begun to organise themselves in Britain and on the European continent prior to 1926. In 1922 Charles ER Bannister, a chiropractor practising in Belfast, had formed the short-lived Chiropractors' Association of the British Isles[56]. 1924 saw the first publication of the *Chiropractoren* (The Chiropractor) in Denmark, which was possibly the first European chiropractic periodical[57]. In 1925 2 associations of chiropractors that continue to exist to this day came into being, the British Chiropractors' Association (BCA) and the Danish Chiropractors' Association[58-59]. 1925 also saw the formation of an association of chiropractic patients in Denmark. Originally

Table 1. The chapter headings from the book Healing by Manipulation (Bone-setting) by J Henry Jones, published in 1926

Forward
I. An introduction to chiropractic
II. The principle of chiropractic
III. Will it work?
IV. Limitations of chiropractic
V. The history of chiropractic
VI. An appeal to the medical profession

(From Jones JH. Healing by Manipulation (Bone-setting). London: Watts and Company, 1926)

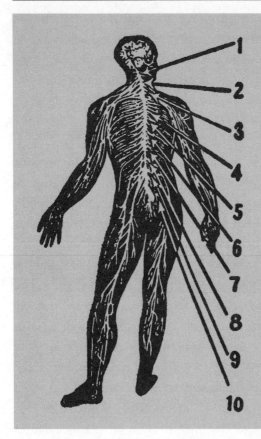

The Chart indicates some of the chief centres of nerve-pressure, but it is impossible to give a complete list of complaints that can be treated by chiropractic.

1. Displacements at this point cause locomotor ataxia, deafness, ringing in the ears, diseases of the eyes, epilepsy, insomnia, wry-neck, vertigo, facial paralysis, loss of memory, delirium.
2. Displacements at this point cause neuralgia, goitre, dizziness, catarrh, heart troubles, complaints of the pancreas, spleen, lungs, and thyroid gland.
3. Displacements at this point cause bronchitis, rheumatism, pains in the arms and shoulder blades, liver and stomach troubles.
4. Displacements at this point cause pneumonia, asthma, tuberculosis, difficult breathing, face, skin, and eye diseases, affections of the mammary glands.
5. Displacements at this point cause pleurisy, enlargement of the spleen, tonsillitis.
6. Displacements at this point cause dyspepsia, gall-stones, fevers, worms, shingles.
7. Displacements at this point cause diabetes, floating kidney, Bright's disease, croup, sick headache.
8. Displacements at this point cause peritonitis, lumbago, affections of the bladder, appendicitis, infantile paralysis.
9. Displacements at this point cause sciatica, constipation, catarrh of the bowels, ovarian troubles.
10. Displacements at this point cause troubles of the uterus and sacrum, cramp in the hips, menstrual and uterine disorders.

Figure 14. The figure, adapted from the book, Healing by Manipulation (Bone-setting), by J Henry Jones, describes conditions that some early chiropractors would have believed they could treat

(From Jones JH. In: Healing by Manipulation (Bone-setting). London: Watts and Company; 1926, 58-59)

named Chiropractisk Forening (The Chiropractic Association), it became Chiropractisk Patientforening (The Chiropractic Patients' Association) in 1930. The fact that during the 1920s European chiropractors began to organise themselves into associations for mutual benefit and protection, that they published material relating to their field, and that they mobilised patients in support of their development, distinguished them from their antecedents the bonesetters in a fundamental way. A process of professionalisation had begun within European chiropractic.

For all this, there were divisions within the European chiropractic ranks. In the United States there had been disagreements between those who wished chiropractic to develop in what they perceived to be its *straight*, unadulterated form, and those who wished to *mix* chiropractic with adjunctive therapies. Both DD Palmer, chiropractic's founder, and

BJ Palmer, his son, were opposed to mixing chiropractic with other methods. In 1904 there was criticism for Solon Langworthy from the Palmer School of Chiropractic:

> "Brother L. (sic) it is not necessary to inform the public that you have mixed Chiropractic and Osteopathy; for your literature shows that you use an Osteopath table and a stretching machine. A chiropractor has no use for either of the above appliances. You learned Chiropractic without any adjuncts, during the year of 1901, at the Palmer School of Chiropractic, at Davenport, Ia."[60]

In 1910, in *The Chiropractor's Adjustor: The Science, Art and Philosophy of Chiropractic*, DD Palmer had written:

> "A Chiropractor who comprehends the principles of this science will have no use for adjuncts. Just in proportion as he lacks knowledge and confidence (the two go together) he will use remedies, become a mixer. The more he mixes the less use he has for Chiropractic."[61]

Whereas many of those who called themselves chiropractors and were practising in Europe supported the notion of straight chiropractic as professed by the Palmers, there were others who preferred to view chiropractic as but one element of effective natural therapeutics. In the first chapter of his book *A Healing Crisis*, published in 1933, Floyd McKeon wrote:

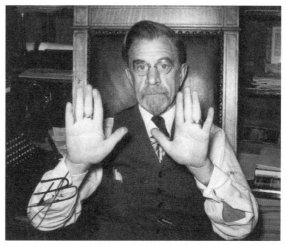

Figure 15. Use of the hands has always been central to chiropractic. BJ Palmer, pictured here in 1947, believed that chiropractic treatment should be given by hand only.

(Courtesy of Lelia Schlabach, DC)

> "Spinal manipulation, osteopathy and chiropractic, are absolutely indispensable to the naturopath ... it is well to bear in mind that the greatest value of spinal manipulation is realised when it is used in conjunction with other forms of treatment at the command of the naturopath."[62]

In Britain during the 1920s and 1930s attempts were made to teach chiropractic within a context of *nature cure*. At least 3 short-lived schools purporting to teach chiropractic were set up[54, 63-64]. In 1921 William Looker started a school in Manchester, originally called the Looker School of Bloodless Surgery, which in 1923 changed its name to the Looker College of Osteopathy and Chiropractic. An educational package that focused more specifically on chiropractic was provided by the British College of Chiropractic from 1925. Its graduates were granted a diploma in chiropractic and were eligible to join the British Chiropractic Society, which was affiliated to the British Naturopathic Association. In Scotland in the 1930s there was the Edinburgh College of Naturopathy, Osteopathy and Chiropractic. According to its prospectus those who successfully completed the course were entitled to diplomas in naturopathy, osteopathy and chiropractic, and were eligible to join the United Association of Osteopaths, Chiropractors and Naturopaths of Great Britain and Ireland. None of these early schools were recognised by the British Chiropractors' Association, which stood for straight chiropractic. As it happened, many of the graduates of these schools elected to call themselves osteopaths or naturopaths, rather than chiropractors.

In spite of the Great Depression which gripped Europe at the beginning of the 1930s, chiropractic's development continued. A series of new periodicals appeared. Between 1930 and 1931 a journal called *The Chiropractor* was published in England. 1931 saw the first publication of *The Brussels Chiropractor* in Belgium and *The Progressive* in England. Whereas *The Chiropractor* proclaimed the benefits of chiropractic to those unfamiliar with it, and included many case studies, *The Brussels Chiropractor* and *The Progressive* were aimed at chiropractors, rather

The Chiropractor

Vol. I.   DECEMBER 11th, 1930.   No. 7

A CASE OF HIP TROUBLE.
How a Very Confident Prophecy went Astray.

Prophecy is always a little risky, and it is at the best rather a thankless business- for if your prophecy proves right nobody will remember it, and if it proves wrong nobody will forget it. The only safe course is to follow the example of the hen—that wise bird does not prophesy any egg, until after the egg has happened.

And yet in the case of Mr. Emlyn Roberts the medical prophecy seemed a very safe and sure one. At the age of 10 or 11 he displayed unmistakable symptoms of some form of hip disease. In due time a marked curvature developed in the spine—obviously as an indirect result of the hip trouble. The spinal area affected by the curvature became inflamed and extremely tender, and the patient suffered great pain in this region. Rightly or wrongly—(and as to this we have our own opinion) the curvature was diagnosed as T.B, of the spine, and was treated as such. Then came months of lying on a plank; months in various sanitaria; and the patient's outlook on life was absolutely hopeless. His mother resolutely refused to countenance an operation; and finally there came the prophecy to which we have referred—"A cripple for life at 21, if you live." That was all that the future held for Mr. Roberts at this stage, according to the highest available medical authority.

As a last resort the sufferer placed himself in the hands of a chiropractor. According to Chiropractic principles the cause of the trouble would be found in a displacement, slight or serious, of one of the bony segments involved, and this proved in fact to be the case. The offending segment was soon located, and so marked had been the displacement that after the first adjustment Mr. Roberts was able to dispense with the surgical boot which he had been wearing, and was able also to walk in a normal manner. From then on he never looked back. As the primary trouble was corrected, the resulting curvature straightened out, and all pain in the spine gradually disappeared. To-day he is in the best of health, and is in fact in active work preaching the Gospel as an evangelist in his native Wales. And thus another prophecy—a tragic and a sombre one at that—has very happily gone west.

Mr. Roberts's history serves to bring out in rather a striking fashion the value of Chiropractic, in the hands of a competent practitioner, in simplifying and straightening out what appears to be on the surface a tangled, difficult, and complicated case. It is now a well established fact that where practical problems are concerned, the simpler your solution is the more likely is it to be effective. This applies to the very practical problem of getting sick people well. In the case

now under notice the chiropractor went to work at once on the CAUSE of the trouble, and he enabled the patient to stand, and walk, and live a normal life, by restoring to him his own natural, inherent strength and power. That was more simple, and perhaps less impressive-looking, than the idea of building an elaborate artificial apparatus to act as an external support, but it was infinitely more effective. Chiropractic is direct and practical, because, as we have said, it goes straight to the root cause of the trouble. But simple as it is in principle, it has been proved the right method to follow by the fact that no other health method in history has a record of such rapid growth, and none has so high a percentage of health recoveries. And one of its crowning glories is the fact that, as here, it achieves these successes in countless cases where the patient has been definitely, solemnly, and authoritatively assured that he was "incurable." As in Mr. Roberts's case, the chiropractor succeeds when the best that others can do has failed,

Figure 16. The Chiropractor was one of the first chiropractic periodicals to be produced in Europe. It was published between 1930 and 1931.

than a wider audience. The editor of *The Progressive*, Robert Richards, was particularly forthright:

> "Might I be allowed to emphasise the fact that the "PROGRESSIVE" is intended for Chiropractors only, it is not a waiting room paper."[65]

PART 2

Seventy-five years of history: chiropractic in Europe in the years following the birth of the European Chiropractic Union

6. Formation of the European Chiropractic Union

In the context of chiropractic's European history, the formation of the European Chiropractic Union in 1931-1932 stands as a very important landmark.

In May 1931 the British Chiropractors' Association held its 6th Annual Conference in London[66]. On 23rd May there was a dinner to which chiropractors from across Europe were invited. Twenty-one visiting chiropractors joined members of the BCA at the dinner. Afterwards there was an informal meeting at which the possibility of establishing a pan-European organisation was discussed. It was largely due to the efforts of Elsie L Hancock, a British chiropractor, and Charles O Regli, a Swiss chiropractor, that this meeting was arranged, although according to the Belgian chiropractor Henri Gillet the idea of forming a union of chiropractors in Europe had originally come from a Dane[67]. As a result of the meeting a committee was formed, chaired

Figure 17. Chiropractors at dinner in London, July 1932. It was at the London conference of 1932 that the constitution of the ECU was approved and its officers elected.

Table 2. Constitution of the European Chiropractic Union

Article 1. Name. The Name if this Organization shall be the EUROPEAN CHIROPRACTIC UNION, initials, E.C.U.

Article 2. Object. The object shall be the Union of the practicing chiropractors in Europe, for their professional welfare, and for the promotion and expansion of Chiropractic in Europe.

Article 3. Ways. 1. The promotion of chiropractic meetings and associations.
2. The soliciting and filing of any printing and information on Chiropractors, Chiropractic, and things of Chiropractic interest in Europe.
3. The creation of a weekly or monthly paper, for the members, in English, and in which those members will have the right to write under the control of the editor.
4. The Procuring and spreading of Chiropractic propaganda.
5. The promotion of a chiropractic school in Europe.
6. The promotion of legal recognition, and the maintenance of the purity of Chiropractic in Europe.

Article 4. Meetings. Meetings will be arranged at least every two years, by the Executive committee, who will also chose (sic) the time and place.

Article 5. Membership shall be divided into three classes – namely, active; passive; and honorary.
Active. Any qualified chiropractor practicing in Europe, with a diploma from a state recognized school, which school must be approved by the Executive Committee.
Passive. Any Chiropractor not practicing, or doing so out of Europe, or any person not practicing chiropractic but who possess the requisite qualifications and interest in the chiropractic profession. They have no vote.
Honorary. Anyone whom the E.C.U. may be pleased to honor because of services rendered to chiropractic. Affirmative vote of nine-tenths shall be required to elect.

Article 6. Executive committee, Officers, election, and duty. The elective officers shall be elected for two years and until their successors shall be duly elected and qualified. Each country shall also elect a correspondant (sic) or representative of their Chiropractic Organization.
The President shall preside at meetings and have the power to organize special meetings if required, and to elect members to temporary offices when the occasion requires it.
The Vice-President shall act in case of absence or disability of the President, treasurer, or secretary.
Secretary shall be the filing, recording, corresponding, and executing officer of the Union. He shall keep record of all the proceedings, and report at each meeting. He shall also notify the members of meetings and of any other valuable information.
Treasurer shall be the custodian of all funds and property belonging to the Union. He shall collect all the fees and keep record of all money received and disbursed and report the conditions of finances to the meetings of the assembly. He shall deposite (sic) all money in the name of the Union in a State Bank of his country. No money shall be drawn, or paid, or any cheques issued unless a voucher is first made out by both the Treasurer and President.
The representative or correspondant (sic) of each country may be elected if present at the meeting or not, and shall be chosen by the assembly of the Union in case his respective country does not possess any chiropractic organization. He shall co-operate with the Executive committee, and keep it in touch with every event of chiropractic interest in his country.

Article 7. Dues. There shall be 10 swiss francs entrance fee, and the same amount yearly beginning from the date of application. The expenses of the Union shall be paid out of this fund.

Article 8. Official Organ. When deemed feasible there shall be created "The E.C.U. Official Bulletin", and an editor appointed by the assembly. The membership directory shall be published in the Bulletin at least once a year.

Article 9. Proxies legally executed may be voted at any meeting of the Union. Members may vote by mail on issues raised by the President.

Article 10. This Constitution or any part there of may be altered or amended by a three-fourths majority of the total membership.

by Charles Regli, with the object of definitely organising a European Chiropractic Union (ECU). With Regli on this committee were Jules Gillet from Belgium, Thomas Mapp from Britain and Einar Rames from Denmark.

In July 1932 chiropractors again travelled from across Europe to London[68]. BJ Palmer and his wife Mabel were also in attendance. Two informal meetings were held on 2nd July, one in the morning and one in the afternoon, at which a constitution for the ECU was discussed and a draft document produced. On Friday 8th July 1932, 27 chiropractors from 12 different countries met formally to approve the constitution of the ECU and appoint its officers. This process was completed successfully. Charles Bannister was elected the first President of the ECU, Elsie L Hancock its first Vice President, and Charles Regli its first Secretary. An Advisory Committee consisting of representatives from 11 European nations was established and the meeting was then adjourned. At a further meeting the next day, BJ Palmer was elected Honorary Member of the ECU. So it was that chiropractors from across Europe came together for the first time to ensure their welfare, and for the promotion and expansion of chiropractic in Europe.

7. Pre-war years

Following the events of 1931-1932 there would have been a new sense of solidarity amongst many of the chiropractors in Europe. The periodical *The Brussels Chiropractor* became *The European Chiropractor* in August 1932,

Table 3. Approximate number of chiropractors practising in Europe in 1934

United Kingdom and Ireland	90
Denmark, Norway and Sweden	60
Switzerland	12
Germany	12
Belgium	7
France	6
Others	7

From: Gillet HJ. Chiropractic in Europe: a summary of the existing conditions abroad. The Chiropractic Journal 1934; 3 (3), 6-7.

under the editorship of Henri Gillet[69]. Another periodical, *The European Chiropractic Bulletin*, the official organ of the ECU, was first published in November 1932. In the summer of 1933 members of the ECU met in Paris, at which time a common code of ethics was agreed upon[70].

It is appropriate to recognise, however, that the ECU did not represent all who called themselves chiropractors in Europe during the 1930s. In fact, it almost certainly represented only a minority. According to Henri Gillet there were approximately 200 chiropractors in Europe in 1934[71], but the ECU had only 60 members in 1935[72]. In the cause of chiropractic advancement, the ECU deliberately forged a division between those who were considered *qualified* by the Union and those that were not, and a division between those who practised *straight chiropractic* and those who did not:

"The policy of the E.C.U. is for the

Development and Advancement of Straight Chiropractic along Scientific and Practical lines, it admits any Qualified Chiropractor, practising in Europe into its ranks …"[73]

If Gillet is correct, in 1934 there were about 60 chiropractors in England, more than in any other single European nation. Gillet stated that this number reflected similarity in living conditions and language with the United States, and also freedom to practise under law. It is true that under Common Law chiropractors in the United Kingdom were accorded a measure of freedom that distinguished them from their colleagues in many other European nations. A combination of medical opposition and systems of law that were not advantageous to the development of chiropractic almost certainly hampered its growth in a number of countries, including Belgium, France, the Netherlands and Switzerland. Chiropractors were accused of illegally practising medicine. A number were forced to give up their chiropractic practices. There were cases where chiropractors were required to pay fines. At least one went to prison. The following is taken from a letter written by the chiropractor Simon Müller, who in September 1933 was serving a 45-day sentence in the district jail of Meilen, Switzerland:

"My dear Lady, Thanks for your kind card, the encouragement fortified, helped me indeed to overcome that tiresome, semi-dark sitting in a 2 x 3 m. room. Heavy doors, a little window, strongly barred and high up, pretty near unreachable, only by standing on the only stool, one may get a little fresh air. I only see the skies; cobwebs and spiders are the only friends in this place. The "toilette" is right in this small room, consisting in an old bucket, ill smelling and a jar of water with it. Kindly pardon me … I know it is not gentlemanlike to describe such terrible conditions. The warden is very kind. My good wife is allowed to bring me food once a day. Of course that is a privilege. If I would have to eat the things served here, I would go on hunger strike. Hardly would I want to mistreat my god-given system with such food!! If the fight for the sick to get well his own way is natural and correct, then it is also right to empty the bitter cup, given to me to the last of the dregs.

I am not complaining. I will keep on fighting for the right of the sick of getting well. Is there anywhere better a mission to be fulfilled by a common mortal? I am sorry for my wife and my little one year old son. They, of course, suffer through my fate."[74]

In response to the difficulties faced by chiropractors in Europe an emergency fund was set up by the ECU in 1933 for the benefit of chiropractors in trouble, distress, or otherwise[75]. In 1935 the Union appointed its first legal advisor, TSN Warrick, a solicitor from Northern Ireland[76]. Chiropractors practising in Switzerland faced a particularly

Figure 18. Simon Müller, who in 1933 was imprisoned for practising chiropractic in Switzerland

demanding struggle for acceptance under law in the years prior to World War II, but they and their supporters rose to the challenge[77-78]. Chiropractic became recognised as an independent method of healing in the Canton of Lucerne in 1937. Following a process of political agitation in the Canton of Zurich, the issue of legal recognition for chiropractic was put to a public vote in January 1939. Chiropractors and their allies campaigned to persuade the public to vote yes, in the face of significant medical opposition. In the event, 72,000 people voted in favour of chiropractic, 56,000 against. The Swiss Cantons of Lucerne and Zurich were the first European jurisdictions in which chiropractic received specific statutory recognition.

Towards the end of the 1930s the threat of war loomed over Europe. Following ECU conventions in London, Paris, Brussels, and Geneva, plans were made for chiropractors to meet in Berlin in 1937, but the meeting was cancelled following a ballot of ECU members[79]. In spite of this, an ECU convention did take place in Berlin in 1938, attended by 19 chiropractors. The October issue of *The European Chiropractic Bulletin* reported:

"We went to Berlin anyway, and had a darn good meeting. Were we scared? Well maybe a little, but we said the E.C.U. would meet, and it <u>met</u>."[80]

In 1939 the European Chiropractic Union was registered as a British trade union as the *European Chiropractors' Union*[81]. Arrangements were also made whereby members of the Union could be insured against malpractice[82].

Then, on 1st September 1939, German troops crossed the border between Germany and Poland. Two days later, Britain and France were at war with Germany. In January 1940 Charles Bannister, who had been ECU President since its inception, wrote to Henri Gillet outlining his wishes for the period of the War:

"A All members of the Union, must be kept together, and in touch with through the Bulletin, whether their assessment has been paid or not.

B A general moratorium is extended to all members of the Union, who are financially hit, or cannot pay their assessment, till the end of the war.

C All items that pertain to the E.C.U. or

Figure 19. Charles Bannister, the first and longest serving President of the European Chiropractic Union (standing), with members of the Union at a meeting in Copenhagen, 1939

Chiropractic, must be held over till after the war, when they will be brought up, at the first General meeting held."[83]

8. War and its aftermath

"The last issued of the Bulletin Vol. 8 No 5 was sent out on 15th of June 1940, just after France and Belgium were invaded; and in spite of every effort to keep Chiropractors in contact with each other, the ECU had to become dormant. It was also at this time that the Battle of Britain took place, and Britain itself was threatened with invasion. Many had, as the result, to seek refuge in the country away from the dangers of bombing, while others joined the Fighting Forces, both for Over-seas and Home Defence, some also had their homes bombed and some were killed. During all this time the Bulletin had to lie low …

Between that date and the end of 1944, excepting for an odd letter from the Chiropractors in Britain, and a few from Chiropractors in America there was absolutely no news what so-ever of Chiropractors, and those on the Continent were completely cut off.

Several times contact was tried to be made with Chiropractors in Switzerland, but without result.

It was only after the beginning of 1945 that contact was at last made with one or two Chiropractors on the Continent of Europe, and since then a new directory was slowly made out in which the names and addresses of all those who could be contacted were listed."[84]

These words, written by Charles Bannister in 1946, tell us something of the impact of World War II on chiropractic in Europe. After the War the ECU was faced with the challenge of re-organising itself at a time when it was suffering from a lack of new blood, emigration, death, and an increasing average age amongst its practitioners[85]. Bannister, who was still President of the ECU, was now 60 years old and thinking of retirement[86].

These were difficult times. During the War and in the period immediately following it, it had been extremely hard, if not impossible, for prospective students to travel from Europe to the United States to study chiropractic and there were no chiropractic schools in Europe recognised by the ECU. The Swiss had given serious consideration to establishing a chiropractic school, but it had not materialised[78,87]. In 1948, restrictions on currency exchange still existed in much of Europe, but the Swiss were able to transfer funds to the United States. Their response to the problem of education was to provide financial assistance to those who were willing to study chiropractic in the United States, but this was not a workable solution in other European nations.

Danish chiropractors attempted to solve the problem of education in a different way. They decided to establish a temporary chiropractic school in Denmark[88-89]. In September 1948 a single class of 15 students began their studies to become chiropractors. Having sought unsuccessfully to establish co-operation with the medical profession, the 15 *chiropractic students* were asked to enrol as medical students at the University of Copenhagen, in order that they might learn the basic sciences necessary to their education as chiropractors. The University of Copenhagen was not informed of the intent of these students to become chiropractors. According to Simonsen *et al*[88], when 15 medical students left the medical

Figure 20. Cartoon from 1942, as it appeared in the Journal of the National Chiropractic Association. As in the First World War, chiropractors from North America supported the European war effort during the Second World War.

Figure 21. Staff, students and supporters of the temporary Danish chiropractic school, circa 1951

programme, only to graduate as chiropractors 6 months later, university administrators were "quite upset".

Belgian chiropractors also considered teaching chiropractic and establishing a school[87], an idea which was not well received by BJ Palmer when he came to hear of it. In a letter to the chiropractor Arthur Scofield, Palmer was critical of the Belgian chiropractor Henri Gillet:

> "His idea of teaching chiropractic to students is a detriment to our profession.

But, you'll never convince him of that.

As to starting a school: This has been given MUCH thot (sic) for MANY years. It is a question of whether BRAINS AND ABILITY can be divided between two or more places; or whether it had best be concentrated at ONE place and turn out real, genuine, unadulterated, pure CHIROPRACTORS. Yes, so far as schools are concerned, we could start them at various places. This would mean that I would have to divide my Faculty between here and there, divide MY attention between here and there and thus weaken ANY AND ALL such places. I have always taken the position, it is better to specialise and concentrate at ONE place and do a real banged-up good job. This IS what HAS made The PSC what it is – THE FOUNTAIN HEAD SCHOOL, the ONE place ALL could look to and point to with pride – such as you do."[90]

Palmer was probably not best placed to understand the situation in Europe after the War. Before the conflict many European chiropractors had followed his lead in an almost childlike way on matters chiropractic, but times were changing.

In Britain a small number of chiropractors took it upon themselves to take on apprentices. E Russell Llewellyn, an ex-President of the British Chiropractors' Association, was one such person. In 1947 he wrote:

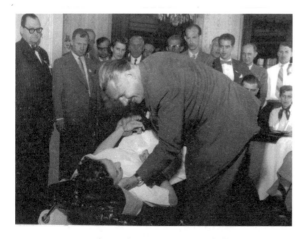

Figure 22. Belgian chiropractor Henri Gillet, demonstrating a chiropractic adjustment, circa 1954

"My reason for undertaking the training of two people is not to establish a one man school, for personally I certainly have not the ability to teach the basic sciences so essential to a complete understanding of the Chiropractic Principle. The reason I embarked on what I am doing is briefly that here in England with an ever growing demand for Chiropractic service we are from month to month faced with an ever dwindling number of Chiropractors to satisfy that demand. Since December of last year we have lost five Chiropractors by emigration and one by death and there is still another one contemplating moving to South Africa. These facts plus the knowledge that the medical profession are gradually accepting, adopting and even teaching our work leads me to the conclusion that desperate needs require desperate deeds." [91]

Another person to take on apprentices was Mary Walker[92]. In 1947 Joan Nind began to study under her. Joan Nind was followed by John McTimoney. In 1949 Mary Walker attempted to set up a chiropractic school. An announcement was made in *The European Chiropractic Bulletin* that a school was to open in Oxford, England, with Mary Walker as its Principal[93]. Initially the editor of *The Bulletin*, Henri Gillet, thought this good news, but feedback from Robert Beech, the editor of the *British Chiropractors' Association Journal*, was far from positive:

"I have no knowledge of the Oxford

*Figure 23. Mary Walker, a chiropractor from England,
who took on two apprentices in the years following
World War II*
(Courtesy of Stan Harding)

Chiropractic School and I am quite sure that the B.C.A. has no knowledge of it either. I understand that several years ago Miss Walker was a member of the B.C.A. but owing to a Breach of "regulations" she either resigned or was asked to resign."[94]

In the absence of backing from the British Chiropractors' Association, Mary Walker's school did not open. In fact, at the time the BCA was itself exploring other avenues to ensure chiropractic's future in the British Isles. It had been involved in discussions with naturopaths and osteopaths with a view to opening joint schools of chiropractic and naturopathy[95-96], but by November 1949 the BCA had come to the conclusion that there was no useful purpose to be served by pursuing the discussions any further[97]. Although the discussions did not result in a significant long

term working relationship between chiropractic, naturopathic and osteopathic organisations in Great Britain, in the interests of survival, the BCA had shown openness towards mixing that would have been almost inconceivable before the War. There would be no turning back.

The period between 1939 and 1951, the War and its aftermath, was one of transition for chiropractic in Europe. On the whole, the chiropractors of Europe responded to the problems that they faced after the War within their own individual nations. International unity was lacking. Having announced his wish to step down as President of the ECU in 1946, Charles Bannister formed an Executive Committee to manage the organisation, and then took a long holiday to Canada, where he had spent his youth[86]. On his return he was disheartened by what he perceived as apathy towards reconstruction of the ECU:

"And above all the chiropractors on the European Continent do not seem to be a bit anxious or interested in reestablishing the ECU, or getting the executive committee to work, that was formed a year ago before I left for Alberta. So what am I to think?

It would therefore seem that the ECU is dead, and as such will remain dead. I have written to many Chiropractors and get no reply. Hence will now quit writing, and start something else. This to me is not a very bright outlook. Now that the war is over, and things should be getting started again."[98]

9. The new European Chiropractic Union

As it turned out, the ECU was not dead, merely sleeping, but it took until 1951 for the chiropractors of Europe to once again unite under the common banner of the Union. In that year chiropractors met in Copenhagen. Representatives from Austria, Belgium, Denmark, France, Norway, Sweden, Switzerland and the United Kingdom agreed to reform the European Chiropractic Union, with the purpose of promoting and defending chiropractic in Europe[99].

In light of previous experience, it was decided that the new ECU should be a union of national associations, rather than a union of discrete individuals as it had been in the past, setting it on what it was hoped would be a more secure basis than that of the old ECU[100]. It was to be run by an Administrative Council consisting of the President, Secretary and Treasurer, who at their discretion, and at least once a year, would convene a General Council consisting of delegates nominated from the

Figure 24. Chiropractors at dinner in Copenhagen in 1951, at the time of the reformation of the ECU

national associations of Europe. Membership of the Union was to be confined to chiropractors who were members of these national associations, the only exception being where a national association did not exist in a given country, in which case an individual practitioner might apply and be eligible for membership of the Union. Others were to be excluded.

The Swiss chiropractor Fred W Illi was elected President of the Union on 4th June 1951. Where the first President of the ECU, Charles Bannister, was, beyond his role as President, primarily a chiropractic clinician, its second President, Fred Illi, was both a clinician and a researcher. In the early 1940s, following failure to establish a chiropractic school in Switzerland, Illi had set up an Institute for the Study of Statics and Dynamics of the Human Body, in Geneva[101]. The development of the Institute, and Illi's work in relation to it, epitomised the beginning of a new European emphasis on scientific research for the understanding and legitimisation of chiropractic.

Bannister and Illi also differed in their relationship with BJ Palmer. Under Bannister, the ECU had been largely subservient to the wishes of the younger Palmer. The ECU under Illi was not. A particular example of the different relationship that Illi had with Palmer is seen in Illi's response to an issue that presented itself in 1954. In that year a debate ensued after BJ Palmer received an invitation from a group of medical doctors in Germany

Figure 25. Celebrations in Copenhagen in 1951. In this photograph, chiropractor Gaston-Lucien Gross (France), is lifted by Svend Buaas (Denmark).

to lecture to them[102]. Not wishing to see chiropractic techniques fall into the hands of these medical doctors, there was concern amongst European chiropractors when Palmer was seen to give the invitation serious consideration. In his correspondence with Palmer, Illi suggested that Palmer was a "quisling". Palmer did not go to Germany, but the *German issue*, as it became known, caused tension between a number of European chiropractors and BJ Palmer. As Gaucher-Peslherbe put it:

"... the German issue had helped to sever the umbilical cord of devotion to B.J. Palmer's person."[103]

Bartlett Joshua Palmer died on 21st May 1961, at the age of 78. At his funeral he was described as a legend in his own time, a representative of the disappearing era of the rugged individualist[104].

10. A changing paradigm of chiropractic

The initial years following the reformation of the ECU were difficult years for the organisation, as the Union reorganised itself and sought the allegiance of Europe's national chiropractic associations[100]. With its core structures in place, and having achieved extensive support from the chiropractic associations of Europe, attention turned to such issues as the relevance of traditional chiropractic doctrines to the modern world, the appropriate scope and means of chiropractic practice, and the need for a European chiropractic school. Within the new ECU there was a more relaxed attitude to those who chose not to practise *straight chiropractic*. There was a spirit of change within the Union, of openness, a wish to make chiropractic relevant to the day.

It had been more than 50 years since Daniel David Palmer had performed his first chiropractic adjustment. At one time chiropractors had made bold claims for their

Figure 26. Swiss chiropractor, Fred Illi, pictured here in the mid-1950s, is probably best known for his contribution to chiropractic research, particularly in relation to spinal biomechanics and the sacro-iliac joints

art, going so far as to consider it a panacea, but it had become increasingly apparent that it was not. In 1961, the Norwegian chiropractor, Arne Gjocih, wrote:

"Concerning chiropractic as a cure for all, it must be assumed that all modern chiropractors do understand their healing art is of a rather limited scope.

To specialise in the treatment of rather few disorders is the tendency today. In this connection one should not underestimate the common sense of the plain people. The man in the street soon will gather facts by experience and make up his mind what kind of treatment is good for his complaints."[105]

More and more, chiropractors were centring their care of patients on a limited number of conditions, especially those of a musculoskeletal nature, viewing chiropractic as but one part of the jigsaw of effective healthcare provision. There were calls for chiropractors to re-evaluate their discipline

Figure 27. Joseph Janse, a chiropractor of Dutch decent, served as President of National College of Chiropractic in Chicago from 1945 until 1983. As well as being recognised as an educator, he is recognised for his contribution to chiropractic research. Janse and Illi shared a common interest in spinal and pelvic biomechanics. Photograph, circa 1949.

along scientifically defensible lines, encourage rational and empirical approaches, and discard traditional metaphysical beliefs[106-107].

In 1961 a European chiropractic journal that might be described as being scientific and academic in the modern sense of these words, was published in Switzerland. The *Annals of the Swiss Chiropractors' Association* concerned itself with theoretical and practical issues in chiropractic, and attempted to exclude material of a speculative, or purely hypothetical nature[108]. Amongst the articles published in the first issue of the journal were papers by Henri Gillet and Maurice Liekens, chiropractors from Belgium, on *motion palpation*[109-110]. Gillet had theorised that the chiropractic spinal lesion, the vertebral subluxation, might be best understood in terms of motion, or the lack of it. He argued that one vertebra might become fixed or restricted relative to an adjacent vertebra, and that it was restriction in movement, or *fixation*, rather than mal-position, that was the key to understanding the subluxation. This was not the first time that Gillet had published material relating to motion analysis of the subluxation, as during the 1950s he had produced *Belgian Notes on Fixation*, but the production of material for the *Swiss Annals* undoubtedly brought his work to the attention of a wider audience. Theories and research into spinal motion marked a departure from the focus on vertebral mal-position that had been central to the teachings of the Palmers. New ideas were challenging old ones.

11. Refining the Constitution: the European Chiropractors' Union

Of the nations of Europe in which chiropractic was practised during the early 1960s, Denmark stands out as a country where chiropractors were particularly successful in rallying public support for their efforts to achieve positive recognition by the state. In 1963 the Chiropractic Laymen's Association in Denmark had over 30,000 members[111]. Nonetheless, there can be little doubt that within Europe it was the chiropractors of Switzerland who had made the greatest advances in terms of their acceptance within society and under law. By 1963 chiropractic was recognised by legislation in 15 Swiss cantons, covering an area populated by approximately 70% of the Swiss people[78]. In March 1964, chiropractic was recognised under Federal Law in Switzerland. Chiropractors were granted the right to practise as independent practitioners whose treatments could be paid for by health insurance policies in those cantons where the discipline was legally regulated.

One might think that during 1963 and 1964 the attention of chiropractors in Switzerland would have been so firmly focused on internal affairs, that they would have had little time to focus on chiropractic's development in Europe as a whole, but this was not the case. At a meeting of the ECU General Council in Ostend, Belgium, in 1963, a motion was put forward by the Swiss representative that the ECU should refine its organisation in order to

Figure 28. Without the support of chiropractic patients and its lay advocates, chiropractic could not exist. In this photograph Ann-Liss Taarup registers WJC Cleave for the 1954 ECU Convention in Copenhagen. More than 50 years on, Ann-Liss Taarup is still promoting chiropractic through her work for ProChiropractic Europe.

better cope with its growing tasks and responsibilities[112]. Given the relative success of Swiss chiropractors and their supporters in developing a position of strength for chiropractic in their homeland, it was to the Swiss Chiropractors' Association that the ECU turned to develop its Constitution in order to make the Union more effective in its workings[113]. Heinrich Buchbinder, a Swiss lawyer who had acted as an advisor to chiropractors in Switzerland for a number of years, was asked to lead the project.

Following a process of consultation, a revised

ECU Constitution was ratified by Union members and came into force on 1st January 1965[114]. It was described by the Swiss chiropractor Flavio Grillo in the *Bulletin of the European Chiropractors' Union* in September 1964:

"The overall picture of the new constitution is characterized by a clearer formulation and more rational structure of the whole work. The paragraphs pertaining to the structure of the E.C.U. have clearly been separated from those concerning its modus operandi, which have been collected in the bylaws.

The objects of the E.C.U. have been broadened and are more specifically defined; they now truly represent a plan of action for the coming years. The General Council is the constituent body of the E.C.U. and consists of the Administrative Council and one representative of each national association; it conducts the business of the E.C.U. and elects the members of the Administrative Council. The voting power of the representatives is proportional to the strength in members of their associations. The Administrative Council remains the executive body of the E.C.U. and comprizes (sic) in addition to the president, the vice-president, the secretary and the treasurer two new members, the chairman of the Professional Council and the editor of the Bulletin. The Bulletin has at last been constitutionally recognised as a periodical publication of the E.C.U. It is

Figure 29. Heinrich Buchbinder, referred to as the "guardian angel" of Swiss chiropractors, who was instrumental in the recognition of chiropractic in Switzerland, and who helped refine the Constitution of the ECU in 1963-1964

(Bulletin of European Chiropractic Union 1964; 4 (7), 19)

edited under the responsibility of the Professional Council, and its editor, which becomes a separate charge from the secretary, is a member of the Administrative and Professional Councils.

An entirely new body has been created under the denomination of the Professional Council. It acts as a committee of the Administrative Council and advises the Administrative and General Councils on all questions concerned with the professional standard, education, legislation and public relations."[112]

The original ECU had been called the *European Chiropractic Union*, and although it had been registered as a British trade union in 1939 as the *European Chiropractors' Union*, it continued to be referred to as the *European Chiropractic Union* until the 1960s. From 1965 onwards, however, notwithstanding the occasional exception, the *European Chiropractic Union* became the *European Chiropractors' Union*, in line with its new Constitution[115].

12. A European chiropractic education

Despite a certain number of political and social successes, even in the 1960s the chiropractors of Europe remained a small group of healthcare practitioners. The ECU Secretary's report for 1962, for example, listed only 221 European chiropractors who were full members of the Union through their national associations[116]. At the heart of the ECU's problem of numbers was education. Those wishing to become chiropractors had to travel to North America to study if they wanted to be associated with the ECU, as there was no school in Europe recognised by the Union at which prospective chiropractors could train.

The problem of education was one that was acknowledged by leading figures within the European chiropractic community. The idea of setting up a school in Geneva was discussed at a forum in Switzerland in 1963[117], but by that time chiropractors in Britain had already taken the matter into their own hands and were actively working towards the establishment of a school in England, a project which many Swiss chiropractors came to support. In 1960 the *Anglo-European College of Chiropractice Limited* had been registered as a charitable organisation[118]. Between 1960 and 1965, Robert Beech, Donald and Elizabeth Bennett, and others, worked to rally support in Britain and on the Continent, and to build up the necessary funds to make their vision of a chiropractic school a reality.

In 1964 the British Chiropractors' Association announced the purchase of premises in Bournemouth for the establishment of the Anglo–European College of Chiropractice (AECC)[119]. The curriculum of the new school was to be based upon the North American model, especially that of Canadian Memorial Chiropractic College, with chemistry and physics being taught at Bournemouth's Technical College via a mutual agreement. It was to be a 4-year, full-time course. The honour of forwarding the first completed student application went to Jack Brownrigg, grandson of Charles Bannister, the ECU's first President[120].

When the AECC opened to students for the first time in September 1965, it did so with the backing of the ECU. The *Bulletin of the European Chiropractors' Union* announced:

> "The FIRST Chiropractic College outside of North America has opened its doors!
> After CANADA, EUROPE!

Figure 30. One of the buildings acquired by the Anglo-European College of Chiropractice in Cavendish Road, Bournemouth

The three B's (Beech, Bennett and Bennett) backed by the big B, the British Chiropractors' Association, backed by some of the European chiropractors, principally by the Swiss, backed by the E.C.U. have DONE IT!"[121]

At the end of the first term there were 18 students studying at the AECC: 10 from Britain, 3 from Denmark, 3 from France, one from Belgium and one from New Zealand[122]; however of this first group, only one student, Robert Melvill, went on to graduate from the College in 1969. The main reason for this was

that the AECC suffered from a number of teething problems during its early years, problems that impacted on morale at the College. In January 1967 a lecturer at the School was dismissed, which acted as a catalyst for a student revolt[123]. A number of students left the College to study chiropractic elsewhere, or to pursue alternative careers.

Despite the early difficulties, the AECC overcame the barriers to its continued existence and became a successful institution. In 1969 the *e* was dropped from *chiropractice* in its title, so that the *Anglo-European College of*

Figure 31. Robert Beech, one of the founders of the Anglo-European College of Chiropractice

Chiropractice became the *Anglo-European College of Chiropractic*[124].

The AECC was the first chiropractic school in Europe to be recognised by the international chiropractic community, but as it happened the faculty of the AECC were not alone in their efforts to provide chiropractic education in the United Kingdom during the 1960s. It has already been stated that during the 1940s there were a small number of chiropractors in Britain who took on apprentices, that one of these was Mary Walker, and that Mary Walker's second pupil was John McTimoney. Having completed his apprenticeship under Mary Walker, John McTimoney started his own practice in Banbury, near Oxford. There he developed his own particular approach to manipulative therapy, an approach that has become known as McTimoney Technique[125]. In the years between 1960 and 1964 he trained his son, Russell, in his Technique. Then, in 1972, he founded the Oxfordshire School of

Chiropractic from his practice in Banbury. McTimoney believed in *straight chiropractic*, that the art in its truest form should entail only diagnosis and treatment by hand, as its founder had intended. He set up his School to teach such an approach and organised the teaching in such a way that it was possible for mature students with full-time jobs to study it. McTimoney was not a member of the British Chiropractors' Association and was therefore not a member of the ECU. His School was not recognised by either organisation, who objected to its educational standards.

Whereas graduates from McTimoney's School were ineligible to belong to the ECU, graduates of the AECC were welcomed into it, and in 1976 the bonds between the AECC and the ECU were strengthened further when administrators at the AECC agreed that the College should not only be European in spirit, but actually governed by the ECU[126]. In 1980 the ECU took direct control of the running of the College, through its Board of Governors[127]. Arne Christensen, the President of the ECU at the time, was appointed Dean of the AECC[128].

13. Towards maturation of the discipline

In the first 10 years of its existence, there were 7 graduating classes from the AECC, with a total of 93 graduates in all. During the AECC's second decade, class sizes grew and more chiropractors entered the field having had a European chiropractic education. Between

1976 and 1986 there were 384 graduates from the AECC. With an increase in the number of chiropractors practising in Europe, came expansion of the ECU. Italy joined as a new member of the ECU in 1976[129] and West Germany in 1980[130], so that by the time of its Golden Jubilee in 1982, there were 10 countries represented within the Union: Belgium, Denmark, France, Great Britain, Italy, the Netherlands, Norway, Sweden, Switzerland and West Germany.

During its first 50 years the ECU had matured and become the key representative body of chiropractic in Europe. Chiropractic, examined from the European perspective, had during this period progressed through a series of steps and taken on a number of attributes that might be associated with the special group of occupations that are referred to as *professions*[131-132]. The first chiropractors to practise in Europe had believed that chiropractic offered something of value to humanity. Extensive provision of chiropractic care had been deemed as something worth working towards, and individuals had joined together to make a full-time commitment to that vision. Chiropractors had organised themselves into associations, at national and at international levels. Those associations had formulated ethical codes to regulate relations with patients and colleagues. In time, a successful European school had been established, a school which was recognised by the international chiropractic community. A process of political agitation had led to statutory regulation of chiropractic in

Table 4. Number of chiropractors in the European Chiropractors' Union, 1982

Denmark	163
France	134
Great Britain	134
Switzerland	101
Norway	86
Belgium	58
Sweden	38
Italy	23
The Netherlands	21
West Germany	9
Individual members	2

TOTAL 769

From: European Chiropractors' Union Directory 1982. Individual members from Greece and Ireland. Numbers exclude Associate Members and retired members.

Switzerland, and chiropractors had become increasingly known and respected in other countries, particularly in relation to the diagnosis and treatment of common musculoskeletal disorders, such as back pain. For all this, by the time of the 50th anniversary of the ECU, there was still an insufficient number of chiropractors practising in Europe to have a major impact on the health of the European populace. Chiropractic in Europe existed as a fringe healthcare discipline, with its education outside the university system, and its practice largely excluded from mainstream healthcare. If chiropractic was to flourish in Europe, if it was to be accepted into the mainstream of healthcare, there would need to be further efforts made to increase the number of chiropractic practitioners, the quality of their education, and the scientific basis for the care provided by them.

During the 1980s a series of positive steps were taken within the educational arena. At the beginning of the decade European chiropractors rallied in support of a venture to move the AECC to premises with capacity to accommodate a greater number of students and space to provide for facilities of a higher quality. Following a merger of local catholic schools, the buildings of Boscombe Convent became available and were purchased by the AECC. The new AECC was officially opened in 1982[133-134]. Then, in January 1984, a second European school of chiropractic to be recognised by the international chiropractic community welcomed students for the first time. Nine students began their studies at the Institut Français de Chiropratique[135]. The French School was set up with support from the French Chiropractors' Association, not because of dissatisfaction with the AECC, but because French chiropractors felt it necessary to have a school in their own country in order to challenge the adverse legal environment in which they worked, under which chiropractic could not be practised freely by chiropractors under law, but was instead deemed to be a medical act, only to be practised by medical doctors[136].

With two internationally recognised chiropractic schools in Europe, and with the potential for more European schools to come into existence, the ECU focused attention on ways of promoting excellence in education and training, and ensuring minimum standards. In North America and in Australia there already existed councils responsible for

Figure 32. Arne Christensen, a Danish chiropractor, who in 1982 was President of the European Chiropractors' Union and Dean of the Anglo-European College of Chiropractic

accreditation of chiropractic educational institutions. During the 1980s a series of discussions within the ECU culminated in the formation of a European Council on Chiropractic Education (ECCE). The ECCE was to act as an autonomous accrediting body for chiropractic education in Europe. A Board of Directors was appointed, with the French chiropractor Pierre Gruny as its President. The inaugural meeting of the Board of Directors of the ECCE was held in September 1987[137].

At the same time as efforts were being made to ensure high standards of chiropractic education in Europe, the ECU was also looking to provide an effective foundation for future

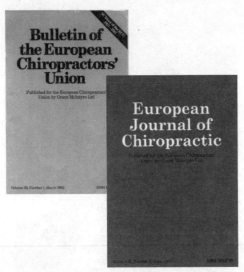

Figure 33. The final issue of the Bulletin of the European Chiropractors' Union and the first issue of the European Journal of Chiropractic, both published in 1982

scientific examination of the discipline. In its Golden Jubilee year, the ECU established a fund to support those who wished to undertake research in the chiropractic field[138]. Efforts were also made to improve the academic standing of the Union's official publication the *Bulletin of the European Chiropractors' Union*. The periodical was given a new name, the *European Journal of Chiropractic*, an Editorial Board was set up, and Grant McIntyre Ltd., an associate company of Blackwell Scientific Publications Ltd., took on responsibility for its publication[139-140].

14. Development of European research into chiropractic

Historically, undertaking research to better understand chiropractic and to improve chiropractic services has presented the European branch of the occupation with a significant challenge, given its relatively small size and limited resources. The first attempts by chiropractors in Europe to provide a scientific grounding for their discipline were few and far between, and often lacked the rigour expected of research today. Gradually, as the discipline grew, so did its focus on research and the quality of the research produced. In this respect, the establishment of the ECU's research fund in 1982 was highly significant. The fund provided a valuable resource that enabled individuals and organisations to undertake research that, in the absence of public funding, would otherwise probably not have been possible. To this day the ECU continues to provide financial support for researchers through its research fund.

Prior to the 1980s, survey research undertaken within Europe had provided a foundation for understanding therapeutic outcomes associated with chiropractic treatment, and a view of the socio-demographic characteristics of chiropractic practice in European context. The Norwegian chiropractor, Øivind Stokke, for example, took it upon himself to survey patients who received chiropractic treatment in the city of Tromsø between 1970 and 1972, in an attempt to understand how their health status changed following chiropractic treatment[141]. His survey of approximately 1,000 randomly selected patients achieved a response rate of 83.5%, with 77% of those who

Figure 34. Alan Breen, 1967 graduate of Canadian Memorial College of Chiropractic, whose research since the 1970s has been instrumental in increasing understanding of chiropractic and providing it with an evidence-base

responded reporting that they were "considerably better" or "completely recovered" from the condition for which they had attended the chiropractor. Between 1973 and 1974, Alan Breen, a British chiropractor, analysed data obtained from 49 practitioner questionnaires, 2,987 case files and 307 patient questionnaires in order to identify major characteristics of chiropractic practice in Britain[142-143]. He concluded that it was a young, growing, and mostly male group of chiropractors who practised in the United Kingdom, that the typical patient was likely to be aged 35-64, of middle social class, and suffering from either low back pain or neck pain for a period longer than 3 months. Breen's study was notable for the fact that its

findings were published in a medical journal, as well as appearing in chiropractic literature.

By the 1980s, it was becoming increasingly clear that if chiropractors in Europe were to accomplish the political objectives to which they aspired, clinical trials comparing the efficacy and effectiveness of chiropractic treatment against other healthcare methods would be required. Arne Christensen wrote:

"Chiropractors are in no doubt as to the value of the service they provide to the community. No chiropractor has been in practice for long, before he or she experiences the dramatic effects that spinal adjustment can have on a person's physiology.

Nobody with a physiological problem, be it a simple musculo-skeletal problem in the low back or a neuromusculo-skeletal problem in the form of aberrant motion in a spinal functioning unit in the lower cervical region causing pain and paraesthesia in the distribution of the ulna nerve, and who has had a chiropractor successfully apply his special skills to the problem, will ever forget the relief chiropractic adjusting can bring to a suffering person.

Individual incidences supported by the opinion of the chiropractors are not enough, however, to change the existing situation in most Western European countries where chiropractic is not

Table 5. Low back pain of mechanical origin: randomised comparison of chiropractic and hospital outpatient treatment. Abstract from a study by the British Medical Research Council.

"Objective:	To compare chiropractic and hospital outpatient treatment for managing low back pain of mechanical origin.
Design:	Randomised controlled trial. Allocation to chiropractic or hospital management by minimisation to establish groups for analysis of results according to initial referral clinic, length of current episode, history, and severity of back pain. Patients were followed up for up two years.
Setting:	Chiropractic and hospital outpatient clinics in 11 centres.
Patients:	Patients aged 18-65 who had no contraindications to manipulation and who had not been treated within the past month.
Interventions:	Treatment at the discretion of the chiropractors, who used chiropractic manipulation in most patients, or of the hospital staff, who most commonly used Maitland mobilisation or manipulation, or both.
Outcome measures:	Changes in the score on the Oswestry pain disability questionnaire and in the results of tests of straight leg raising and lumbar flexion.
Results:	Chiropractic treatment was more effective than hospital outpatient management, mainly for patients with chronic or severe back pain. A benefit of about 7% points on the Oswestry scale was seen at two years. The benefit of chiropractic treatment became more evident throughout the follow up period. Secondary outcome measures also showed that chiropractic was more beneficial.
Conclusions:	For patients with low back pain in whom manipulation is not contraindicated chiropractic almost certainly confers worthwhile, long-term benefit in comparison with hospital outpatient management. The benefit is seen mainly in those with chronic or severe pain. Introducing chiropractic into NHS practice should be considered."

(From Mead TW, Dyer S, Brown W, Townsend J and Frank AO. Low back pain of mechanical origin: randomised comparison of chiropractic and hospital outpatient management. British Medical Journal 1990; 300 (6737), 1431–1437)

recognized by the political system. The politicians who have the responsibility of making decisions also about what type of health care service should be available to the citizens of the individual countries, cannot disregard the existing health care system when they consider how to utilize chiropractic in society. Very often they are faced with having to ask for advice from the people who, at least in the past, have been antagonistic to the whole idea behind chiropractic and the principles of chiropractic, when trying to make decisions on how to incorporate chiropractic care into an already existing health care system.

Where a situation similar to the one

described above has developed, the solution adopted by politicians in several countries has been to ask for clinical trials."[144]

The request for clinical trials had not fallen on deaf ears. In 1981, for example, the United Kingdom's Medical Research Council (MRC) was consulted by the British Chiropractors' Association about the possibility of undertaking research to explore the effectiveness of chiropractic as a treatment for low back pain of mechanical origin[145]. It was agreed that an appropriate way to assess this would be by means of a randomised controlled clinical trial (RCT), in which the effectiveness of chiropractic treatment was compared with hospital outpatient management. Following a feasibility study, a full-scale multi-centre study was undertaken, funded in part by the ECU. The results of the study, which were published in the British Medical Journal in June 1990, suggested that for patients with low back pain in whom manipulation was not contraindicated, chiropractic almost certainly conferred worthwhile, long term benefit in comparison with hospital outpatient management, and that introducing chiropractic into the National Health Service of the UK should be considered[146]. Although the study was criticised for what were seen to be methodological flaws[147-148], it resulted in an increase in the number of new patients attending chiropractors in the UK in the months following its publication[149]. It drew attention to chiropractic and led to political debate about its place within healthcare.

15. Pre-millennial years

The impact of the MRC trial was not confined to Britain, but extended internationally. In a world where cultural, economic, political and social changes were resulting in increased interaction and interdependence between the nations of different continents, chiropractic was not immune. The idea of an organisation to represent chiropractic at global level had been discussed as early as 1962[150], but it was not until 1987, when a first World Presidents' Summit was held in London, that a successful move was made to establish such an organisation. In 1988, a second World Presidents' Summit was held in Sydney, Australia, and the World Federation of Chiropractic (WFC) came into being[151]. Since that time, the WFC has acted as a forum for international discussion and collaboration, and has represented chiropractic on the world stage. In 1997 it entered an official relationship with the World Health Organisation, recognised as a *non-governmental organisation* (NGO).

Within Europe, the late 1980s and the 1990s saw rapid change and development for chiropractic. In Scandinavia, legislation focusing on chiropractic was passed in Norway in 1988, in Sweden in 1989, and in Denmark in 1992. According to the then President of the Danish Chiropractors' Association, Jens Jacobsen, in 1990 there were approximately 250 chiropractors practising in Denmark, serving a population of about 5 million[152].

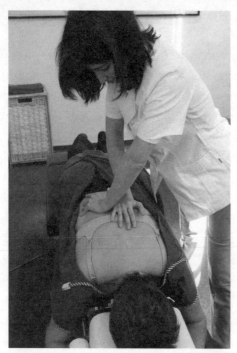

*Figure 35. A chiropractor adjusts a patient
(Courtesy of Asociación Española de Quiropráctica)*

Proportionally, there was approximately one chiropractor to every 20,000 individuals. According to his report, at the time there were in the region of 30,000 people per chiropractor in Norway, 85,000 per chiropractor in Sweden, 40,000 per chiropractor in Switzerland, 200,000 per chiropractor in the UK, 1.5 million per chiropractor in Spain, and 5 million per chiropractor in West Germany.

In 1991 a detailed research survey of chiropractic practice in the countries represented within the ECU was undertaken[153]. With the support of the ECU, the chiropractor Palle Pedersen arranged for 1,290 questionnaires to be mailed to those

listed in the 1990 ECU directory. Chiropractors from what had become 13 member countries of the ECU were surveyed: Belgium, Denmark, Finland, France, Great Britain, Greece, Iceland, Ireland, Italy, the Netherlands, Norway, Sweden and Switzerland. 715 chiropractors responded to the survey, an overall response rate of 55.4%. According to the survey, by 1991 approximately half of the chiropractors who were members of the ECU had been trained in Europe. About a quarter of them were female. European chiropractors were treating mainly musculoskeletal disorders, with little evidence to suggest that organic or visceral conditions were a mainstay of chiropractic practice. Many of the chiropractors worked in collaboration with others, mostly with other chiropractors, but there were a number who shared facilities with healthcare workers from other disciplines. According to the survey, more than 10% of the patients attending chiropractors had been referred by their general medical practitioner, or by a consultant. It would seem that a good number of Europe's medical practitioners had developed a favourable attitude towards chiropractic.

During the last decade of the twentieth century the development of chiropractic education in Europe continued apace. In 1988 the Council for National Academic Awards (CNNA) in the United Kingdom had validated a BSc Chiropractic degree at the AECC, and by 1991 the first graduates were entering the field with the new qualification[154]. Another significant landmark

Figure 36. Her Royal Highness, the Princess of Wales, visiting the Anglo-European College of Chiropractic in 1990

for the School was the successful attainment of Royal Patronage in 1990, the year of its 25th anniversary, when Her Royal Highness, the Princess of Wales accepted an invitation to become Patron of the College[155]. Having become an associate College of the University of Portsmouth, and having perceived a need for formalised post-graduate education, the AECC developed an MSc Clinical Chiropractic in 1996[156]. A year later, its undergraduate programme was upgraded to a 5-year MSc Chiropractic.

The development of Masters level programmes at the AECC was a significant evolution for the School, however, higher chiropractic degrees were also on the agenda in at least one other European country. In Denmark, in 1995, the Minister for Education had granted permission for commencement of the first stage of a 5-year course that would lead to a Masters degree in Clinical Biomechanics for those that successfully completed it, and which would act as a basis from which a licence to practise chiropractic in Denmark might be granted[157]. The new course at the University of Southern Denmark in Odense provided students with what was at the time a unique opportunity to study chiropractic at a European university with public funding. The

Figure 37. A chiropractic technique classroom at the University of Southern Denmark. The establishment of a chiropractic course at the University of Southern Denmark was a landmark in the development of European chiropractic education. For the first time students could study chiropractic at a publicly funded European university.
(Courtesy of Thierry Kuster, DC)

University of Southern Denmark was accredited by the ECCE in 1999.

Back in Britain, 2 new university-based degree courses in chiropractic welcomed students for the first time in 1997, an MSc degree programme at the University of Surrey, and a BSc (Hons) programme at the University of Glamorgan[158-159]. Whereas the course at the University of Surrey was short-lived, the Welsh Institute of Chiropractic at the University of Glamorgan was successful in introducing chiropractic into the publicly

Figure 38. Susan King, the first Head of the Welsh Institute of Chiropractic, pictured with David Byfield, who succeeded her as Head of the School in 2005

funded university system of the United Kingdom[160]. It was accredited by the ECCE in 2002.

Advancements in European chiropractic education during the 1990s were paralleled by successes for chiropractic in the research arena. In 1992 the expression *evidence-based medicine* was coined to signify the process of using best scientific research evidence in decision making about the care of individual patients[161-162]. In its application, increasing evidence in support of the use of manipulation for those suffering with acute low back pain, provided a basis for a series of national clinical practice guidelines to recommend the use of manipulative therapy by chiropractors, osteopaths and physiotherapists as a therapeutic option for those with the condition[163-166]. In 1997 Alan Breen noted that evidence-based practice had been a friend to chiropractic, in so far as it had legitimised much of what chiropractors did[167]. Nonetheless, it also asked questions of it, and some found it wanting. Not everyone agreed that the value of chiropractic had been proved. In an article published in the *British Medical Journal* in 1998, for example, Edzard Ernst and Willem Assendelft argued that on the basis of available evidence, it seemed uncertain whether chiropractic did more good than harm[168].

16. Chiropractic's global identity in the twenty-first century

In the spring of 2001 Paris played host to 750 chiropractors from 48 countries, when the World Federation of Chiropractic held its 6th Biennial Congress there in conjunction with the European Chiropractors' Union and the Association Française de Chiropratique[169]. Except for those medically qualified, the practice of chiropractic remained technically illegal in France, and the Congress presented an opportunity to showcase chiropractic and encourage movement towards its political acceptance. As well as attendance at the academic programme, delegates were invited to visit the new premises of what had been the Institut Français de Chiropratique, but which had been renamed L'Institut Franco-Européen de Chiropratique (IFEC) upon its move in 1999[170]. Despite an absence of legal recognition for chiropractors wishing to practise in France, the Parisian School had continued to train chiropractors in a spirit of liberty in education.

Probably the most important discussions at the Paris Congress concerned identity in chiropractic. North American chiropractic schools had agreed to a unified vision of chiropractic in 1996, the Association of Chiropractic Colleges' (ACC) *Paradigm of Chiropractic*, and that vision was discussed in Paris. Despite opposition from the representatives of a number of European countries who argued that additional time for debate was appropriate, the Assembly of the WFC agreed to adopt the ACC Paradigm by a majority of 68 to 24 votes[171]. According to the ACC Paradigm, the purpose of chiropractic was to optimize health. Based on the principle that the body's innate recuperative power was

**World Federation of Chiropractic's
6th Biennial Congress**
in association with
the European Chiropractors' Union
and the Association Française de Chiropratique

vive la chiropratique!

WFC 6th
Biennial Congress
May 21-26, 2001
Paris, France

**The Science, Art and Philosophy of
Chiropractic Practice from Youth to Age
May 24-26, 2001
Paris, France**

Plan now to attend the Congress in Paris - the City of Light -
and join the largest gathering of Chiropractors from around the world
to hear from leading speakers, participate in innovative workshops
and enjoy the delights of Paris in the springtime!

Figure 39. Advertisement for the World Federation of Chiropractic's 6th Biennial Congress, held in association with the European Chiropractors' Union and the Association Française de Chiropratique

affected by and integrated through the nervous system, the practice of chiropractic included establishing a diagnosis, facilitating neurological and biomechanical integrity through appropriate chiropractic case management, and promoting health.

The coming together of representatives from

across the chiropractic world to reach a consensus on the Paradigm of Chiropractic was a significant moment in chiropractic's development, however, it remained to be seen how everyday chiropractors, practising across the world, viewed their occupation and its public identity. In 2003 a task force was appointed by the WFC to direct and facilitate an international consultation on identity in chiropractic[172]. An electronic survey of chiropractors was conducted. In October 2004, 29,094 chiropractors from 54 countries were e-mailed and invited to take part in the survey. 3,689 responded and completed the survey adequately, a response rate of 12.7%. The Identity Consultation Task Force presented its findings and recommendations to the 8th Biennial Assembly of the WFC in June 2005. At the meeting there was unanimous agreement on the following:

"1. *International Identity.* That the public identity of the chiropractic profession, if it is to be effective and successful, should be similar in all countries.

2. *Three Concepts.* That this identity should be established and maintained through the use of the following three linked concepts:

a. A leading statement on identity, which must be clear, concise and immediately relevant to both the public and the profession – the 'pole' (brand platform).

b. Several important qualifying statements, which provide the necessary context and foundation for the pole – the 'ground' (brand pillars).

c. A description of the qualities or essential personality of chiropractors – the 'personality' (tone).

3. *The Pole.* The pole should be: The spinal health care experts in the health care system.

4. *The Ground.* The ground should be:

a. Ability to improve function in the neuromusculoskeletal system, and overall health, wellbeing and quality of life.

b. Specialised approach to examination, diagnosis and treatment, based on best available research and clinical evidence, and with particular emphasis on relationship between the spine and the nervous system.

c. Tradition of effectiveness and patient satisfaction.

d. Without the use of drugs and surgery, enabling patients to avoid these where possible.

e. Expertly qualified providers of spinal adjustment, manipulation and other manual treatments, exercise instruction and patient education.

Table 6. Twenty-first century definitions of chiropractic

A health profession concerned with the diagnosis, treatment and prevention of mechanical disorders of the musculoskeletal system, and the effects of these disorders on the functions of the nervous system and general health. There is an emphasis on manual treatments including spinal adjustment and other joint and soft-tissue manipulation.

WFC Dictionary Definition, World Federation of Chiropractic, 2001

A health care profession concerned with the diagnosis, treatment and prevention of disorders of the neuromusculoskeletal system and the effects of these disorders on general health. There is a an emphasis on manual techniques, including joint adjustment and/or manipulation with a particular focus on subluxations.

The WHO definition, World Health Organisation, Guidelines on Chiropractic, 2005

f. Collaboration with other health professionals.

g. A patient-centred and biopsychosocial approach, emphasising the mind/body relationship in health, the self-healing powers of the individual, individual responsibility for health, and encouraging patient independence.

5. *The Personality.* The personality should be a combination of:
Expert, professional, ethical, knowledgeable; and accessible, caring, human, positive."[173]

17. Chiropractic in Europe in the twenty-first century

Europeans have been active in chiropractic's global development in recent years. One of the Co-Chairs of the WFC's Identity Consultation Task Force was Peter Dixon, an ex-President of the ECU. Another ex-President of the ECU, Anthony Metcalfe, served as President of the WFC between 2004 and 2006[174]. His presidency saw not only international consensus on identity in chiropractic, but also publication of World Health Organisation Guidelines on Basic Training and Safety in Chiropractic[175]. It seems timely that in the first decade of the twenty-first century, a decade that has been identified by the United Nations and the World Health Organisation as the *Bone and Joint Decade*, that chiropractic should have reached the level of global maturity that it has. It also seems fitting that European chiropractors should have played crucial roles in chiropractic's recent global development, given that during the current decade there are celebrations to mark 100 years of chiropractic in Europe and 75 years of the European Chiropractors' Union.

Within Europe, the first years of the twenty-first century have seen a number of advances for chiropractic. The AECC has developed a professional doctorate programme and now has public funding for its undergraduate course[176-177]. The current decade has also

Figure 40. President and Secretary General of the World Federation of Chiropractic, 2005. Anthony Metcalfe (left) and David Chapman-Smith (right).

Table 7. European Chiropractors' Union Conventions, 1982-2007

1982	Bournemouth, UK
1983	Copenhagen, Denmark
1984	Zürich, Switzerland
1985	Den Haag, The Netherlands
1986	Stockholm, Sweden
1987	London, UK
1988	Rapallo, Italy
1989	Bergen, Norway
1990	Avignon, France
1991	Dublin, Ireland
1992	Marbella, Spain
1993	London, UK
1994	Brussels, Belgium
1995	No convention
1996	Geneva, Switzerland
1997	Amsterdam, The Netherlands
1998	Saint-Vincent, Aosta, Italy
1999	Odense, Denmark
2000	Athens, Greece
2001	Paris, France
2002	Oslo, Norway
2003	Heidelberg, Germany
2004	Helsinki, Finland
2005	Lemesol, Cyprus
2006	Stockholm, Sweden
2007	Vilamoura, Portugal

seen moves to establish new chiropractic schools in Europe, for example, in Norway, where Parliament has recommended establishing chiropractic education in a university setting, and in the Netherlands, where the ECU has granted €75,000 to assist in the development of university-based education[178]. A new organisation, the European Academy of Chiropractic (EAC), was formed in 2006 to govern the academic arm of the ECU, to promote continuing postgraduate development amongst chiropractors, and to liaise with academic institutions approved by the ECU[179]. The first formal meeting of the Academy was held in Stockholm in May 2006, attended by George Carruthers, Secretary General of the EAC, Philippe Druart, President of the ECU, Jean Robert, the Academic Dean of the EAC, and by Flemming Teilman Nielson, the Registrar of the new body. The Academy is the first organisation of its kind set up at European level and will accept into membership only chiropractors with qualifications recognised by the ECCE.

The period between 2000 and 2007 has seen continuing development of research relating to chiropractic. A notable recent research study is the *UK BEAM Trial*, a multi-centred randomised trial which involved 181 general medical practices, and which was intended to examine the effect of adding exercise classes, spinal manipulation, or manipulation followed by exercise to *best care* in general medical practice for patients presenting with back pain[180]. The results of the study, which were reported in the British Medical Journal in 2004, supported the use of physical interventions frequently employed by chiropractors in management of patients suffering from back pain. Specifically, it concluded that relative to *best care* in general medical practice, manipulation followed by exercise achieved a moderate benefit at 3 months and a small benefit at 12 months; spinal manipulation achieved a small to moderate benefit at 3 months and a small benefit at 12 months; and exercise achieved a small benefit at 3 months but not at 12 months. The study suggested that

Table 8. Presidents of the European Chiropractors' Union, 1932-2007

1932–	Charles Bannister, UK
1951–	Fred Illi, Switzerland★
1962–	Aage Pedersen, Denmark
1964–	Pierre Jaquet, Switzerland
1968–	Flavio Grillo, Switzerland
1975–	Gilbert Juan, France
1978–	Arne Christensen, Denmark
1988–	Christoph Diem, Switzerland
1993–	Anthony Metcalfe, UK
1998–	Flemming Teilmann Nielsen, Denmark
2000–	Peter Dixon, UK
2004–	Philippe Druart, Belgium

★Records available for the period between 1951 and 1960 are incomplete and it has not been possible to ascertain whether Fred Illi served as President for the whole of this period.

manipulation would make a cost-effective addition to *best care* in general medical practice[181].

As well as advances and successes for European chiropractic in the initial years of the twenty-first century, there have been, and continue to be, problems and challenges. In 1957 the Treaty of Rome outlined a vision for a European Community that has led to the European Union (EU) that we know today. A principle of the Treaty of Rome was free movement of persons within the European Community, a vision that has still not become a total reality, and which has been particularly problematic in relation to healthcare occupations and other professional groups. Where minimum standards of education are not uniform in all member nations of the EU, free movement poses the danger of reducing standards to the level of the lowest common denominator. In the case of chiropractic, there remain a number of European nations in which the title *chiropractor* is not protected by law and where no minimum standards exist, posing a special danger. In response to the perceived threat, the ECU implemented a process of political lobbying, and has recognised that harmonisation of legislation relating to chiropractic across Europe will be essential if the potential for free movement of chiropractors across the continent is to be successfully acheived[182]. In this respect, agreement between the nations of Europe on minimum educational standards in chiropractic is important. The teaching of *chiropractic* in short courses lasting only a few weekends, as has been documented in articles about Germany and Spain recently, is likely to be detrimental[183-184].

Another issue that the ECU has had to face within the last few years has been the withdrawal of Denmark from the Union at the end of 2003, the Danes having had a number of concerns about the ECU and the way the Organisation functioned[185]. At the time of writing, Denmark remains outside the Union, but efforts are being made to restore its position within the ECU.

18. Celebrating the past, the present and the future of chiropractic

In the spring of 2006 the ECU held its Annual Convention in Stockholm, the theme of the

Table 9. European Chiropractors' Union Awards

Since 2000 the ECU has recognised a small number of chiropractors for their outstanding contributions to chiropractic. They are:

2000	Arne Christensen, Denmark
2001	Alan Breen, UK
2004	John Naef, Switzerland
2006	Charlotte Leboeuf, Denmark

event being *chiropractic: a multifaceted profession.* In the years since its origin, chiropractic has evolved from the ideas and practices of a single magnetic healer in Davenport, Iowa, to become the complex and multifaceted discipline that we know today. Today, chiropractic is practised by nearly 100,000 individuals in various parts of the world, the majority of those calling themselves chiropractors living and working in the United States[186]. Although the chiropractors of Europe remain a relatively small group in relation to their counterparts across the Atlantic, chiropractic in Europe is thriving and the number of chiropractors practising in Europe is growing exponentially. Currently, there are 18

Figure 41. The President of the European Chiropractors' Union, Philippe Druart, with ECU officials, 2006. From left to right: Efstathios (Stathis) Papadopoulos (1st Vice-President), Philippe Druart (President), Anne Kemp (Executive Secretary), George Carruthers (Secretary General of the European Academy of Chiropractic), and John Williams (2nd Vice-President).

*Table 10. Number of chiropractors in the European
Chiropractors' Union, October 2006*

Great Britain	1,284
Norway	364
Switzerland	246
France	215
The Netherlands	193
Italy	180
Sweden	163
Ireland	141
Spain	140
Belgium	96
Germany	63
Finland	44
Greece	25
Portugal	22
Cyprus	10
Iceland	5
Luxembourg	5
Liechtenstein	4

TOTAL Number of chiropractors, 3,200

member nations within the ECU, representing approximately 3,000 chiropractors, who together make up the mainstream of chiropractic in Europe. In the future it seems likely that the ECU will grow to include new member states, possibly expanding its influence into the nations of Eastern Europe.

In May 2007 chiropractors are to meet in Vilamoura, Portugal, to celebrate the past, present and future of chiropractic, at a Conference hosted by the Portuguese Chiropractors' Association. The Conference will combine the World Federation of Chiropractic's 9th Biennial Congress with the ECU's 75th Anniversary Convention, and incorporate meetings of two other global organisations, the Foundation for

Chiropractic Education and Research and the Association for the History of Chiropractic. 2007, the year of the 75th anniversary of the ECU, is an appropriate time for chiropractors in Europe to reflect on their history, consider its lessons, and plan for the future.

References

1. Roba W. The Tri-Cities, 1885–1920. In: The River and the Prairie: A History of the Quad-Cities, 1812–1960. Quad-Cities: The Hesperian Press; 1986, pp. 95–117.

2. Gielow V. Daniel David Palmer: rediscovering the frontier years, 1845–1887. *Chiropractic History* 1981; 1 (1), 11–13.

3. Palmer DD. Journal of Daniel David Palmer; 1868–1892. Archives, Palmer College of Chiropractic.

4. Palmer DD. Day Book of Daniel David Palmer; 1886–1887. Archives, Palmer College of Chiropractic.

5. Burlington City Directory; 1887, p. 267.

6. Biographical Review of Des Moines County, Iowa. Chicago: Hobart Publishing Company; 1905, pp. 230–234.

7. The third generation: Chas E Caster takes up the healing art. Saturday Evening Post of Burlington, Iowa; 17th April 1915, p. 1.

8. Lillard H. Deaf seven years. *The Chiropractic* 1897; January (17), 3.

9. Palmer DD. A brief history of the author and

chiropractic. In: The Chiropractor's Adjustor: The Science, Art and Philosophy of Chiropractic. Portland: Portland Printing House Company; 1910, pp. 17-19.

10. Keating JC. The embryology of chiropractic thought. *European Journal of Chiropractic* 1991; 39 (3), 75-89.

11. Keating JC. The evolution of Palmer's metaphors and hypotheses. *Philosophical Constructs for the Chiropractic Profession* 1992; 2 (1), 9-19.

12. Keating JC. Several pathways in the evolution of chiropractic manipulation. *Journal of Manipulative and Physiological Therapeutics* 2003; 26 (5), 300-321.

13. Palmer BJ. In: The Science of Chiropractic. Reference to S. Weed's naming of chiropractic is made on an unnumbered page at the beginning of the book. Davenport: The Palmer School of Chiropractic; 1906.

14. Still AT. In: Autobiography of A.T. Still. Kirksville: Published by the author; 1897, p. 108.

15. Walter GW. The beginning. In: The First School of Osteopathic Medicine. Kirksville: Thomas Jefferson University Press and Northeast Missouri State University; 1992, pp. 1-16.

16. Palmer DD. Dr. Palmer. *The Chiropractic* 1899; (26), 1.

17. Palmer DD. Preface. In: The Chiropractor's Adjustor: The Science, Art and Philosophy of Chiropractic. Portland: Portland Printing House Company; 1910, pp. 9-16.

18. Palmer DD. Chiropractic not osteopathy. In: The Chiropractor's Adjustor: The Science, Art and Philosophy of Chiropractic. Portland: Portland Printing House Company; 1910, pp. 139-145.

19. Parker HJ. What my neighbor thinks. *The Magnetic Cure* 1896; January (15), 3.

20. Palmer DD. Revolution. In: The Chiropractor's Adjustor: The Science, Art and Philosophy of Chiropractic. Portland: Portland Printing House Company; 1910, pp. 74.

21. Lerner C. The "unreported case" of "Reiring vs. Palmer". In: The Lerner Report: A History of the Early Years of Chiropractic. Circa 1952, pp. 254-265.

22. Palmer BJ. The story of D.D. Palmer – his life, personality, and peculiarities. In: Fight to Climb. Hammond: WB Conkey Company; 1950, pp. 46-81.

23. Zarbuck MV & Hayes MB. Following D.D. Palmer to the west coast: the Pasadena connection, 1902. *Chiropractic History* 1990; 10 (2), 17-21.

24. Dr. T.H. Storey mysteriously disappears. *The Chiropractor* 1905; 1 (2), 12-18.

25. Carver W. Production of an advertiser. In: History of Chiropractic. Circa 1936, pp. 42-46.

26. Keating JC. B.J. Palmer, President (1906-1913). In: B.J. of Davenport: The Early Years of Chiropractic. Davenport: Association for the History of Chiropractic; 1997, pp. 51-84.

27. Palmer BJ. The Science of Chiropractic.

Davenport: The Palmer School of Chiropractic; 1906.

28. Keating JC, Callender AK & Cleveland CS. The first decade, 1896-1906. In: A History of Chiropractic Education in North America. Davenport: Association for the History of Chiropractic; 1998, pp. 1-11.

29. Troyanovich SJ & Gibbons RW. Finding Langworthy: the last years of a chiropractic pioneer. *Chiropractic History* 2003; 23 (1), 9-17.

30. Ferguson A & Wiese G. How many chiropractic schools? An analysis of institutions that offered the D.C. degree. *Chiropractic History* 1988; 8 (1), 27-36.

31. Keating JC, Callender AK & Cleveland CS. The second wave: school proliferation, 1908-1920. In: A History of Chiropractic Education in North America. Davenport: Association for the History of Chiropractic; 1998, pp. 21-32.

32. Kimbrough M. Jailed chiropractors: those who blazed the trail. *Chiropractic History* 1998; 18 (1), 79-84.

33. Bower N & Hynes R. Going to jail for chiropractic: a career's defining moment. *Chiropractic History* 2004; 24 (2), 21-26.

34. Wardwell WI. The Palmers and their Fountainhead School. In: Chiropractic: History and Evolution of a New Profession. St. Louis: Mosby-Year Book, Inc.; 1992, pp. 51-84.

35. Van Raders E. *The Chiropractor* 1905; 1 (5), 4.

36. Van Raders E. *The Chiropractor* 1906; 2 (9-10), 24.

37. *The Chiropractor* 1906; 2 (9-10), 46-47.

38. Heathcote GP. *The Chiropractor* 1906; 2 (9-10), 23.

39. Van Raders E. *The Chiropractor* 1906-1907; 3 (1-2), 44.

40. Van Raders E. *The Chiropractor* 1907; 3 (9-10), 23.

41. U.C.A. Directory. *The Chiropractor* 1908; 4 (7-8), 111-113.

42. Gaucher-Peslherbe PL. Chiropractic as a profession in Europe. *Journal of Manipulative and Physiological Therapeutics* 1992; 15 (5), 323-330.

43. Callahan M. *National Journal of Chiropractic* 1919; January, 22.

44. Anderson R. Indigenous bonesetters in contemporary Denmark. In: Oths KR & Hinojosa SZ, editors. Healing by Hand: Manual Medicine and Bonesetting in Global Perspective. Oxford: Altamira Press; 2004, pp. 5-22.

45. *Gentleman's Magazine* 1736; 6, 618.

46. Moulton T. The Compleat Bonesetter: Wherein the Method of Curing Broken Bones, and Strains, and Dislocated Joints, Together with Ruptures Vulgarly Called Broken Bellyes, is Fully Demonstrated. Whereunto is Added the Perfect Oculist, and the Mirror of Health. Treating the Pestilence, and All Other Diseases Incident to Men,

Women and Children. Also the Acute Judgement of Urines. London: Harrison; 1656.

47. Paget J. Clinical lecture on cases that bone-setters cure. *British Medical Journal* 1867; January 5, 1-4.

48. Hood W. On the so-called "bone-setting", its nature and results. *Lancet* 1871; 97 (2480), 336-338.

49. Hood W. On the so-called "bone-setting", its nature and results (continued). *Lancet* 1871; 97 (2481), 372-374.

50. Hood W. On the so-called "bone-setting", its nature and results (continued). *Lancet* 1871; 97 (2483), 441-443.

51. Hood W. On the so-called "bone-setting", its nature and results (continued). *Lancet* 1871; 97 (2485), 499-501.

52. Hood W. On Bonesetting (So Called) and its Relation to the Treatment of Joints Crippled by Injury, Rheumatism &c. &c. London: Macmillan and Company; 1871.

53. Bennett GM. The Art of the Bone-Setter: a Testimony and a Vindication. London: Thomas Murby; 1884.

54. Collins M. The first 30 years. In: Osteopathy in Britain: The First Hundred Years. Charleston: BookSurge, LLC; 2005, pp. 11-34.

55. Jones JH. Forward. In: Healing by Manipulation (Bone-setting). London: Watts and Company; 1926, pp. 9-11.

56. Bannister CER. The Chiropractors'

Association of the British Isles. *Fountain Head News* 1922; 12 (1), 12.

57. Bak-Jensen ST. Chiropractors and authority in interwar Denmark. In: Manipulative Exclusivity: The Legitimation Strategies of Early Danish Chiropractors, 1920-1943. Copenhagen: PhD Dissertation, University of Copenhagen; 2004, pp. 40-94.

58. Hancock EL. The formation of the British Chiropractic Association. *The European Chiropractor* 1933; 2 (3), 5-7.

59. Hviid MG. Chapman-Smith D, translating editor. History of Chiropractic in Denmark. Toronto: Danish Pro-Chiropractic Association; 1984. [Original text published in Danish; 1975].

60. *The Chiropractor* 1904; 1 (1), 6.

61. Palmer DD. In: The Chiropractor's Adjustor: The Science, Art and Philosophy of Chiropractic. Portland: Portland Printing House Company; 1910, p. 136.

62. McKeon LCF. Natural therapeutics in general. In: A Healing Crisis. Weston-Super-Mare: Michell Health Products; 1933, pp. 28-29.

63. McKeon LCF. Chiropractic in Great Britain. In: A Healing Crisis. Weston-Super-Mare: Michell Health Products; 1933, pp. 139-145.

64. School prospectus. Edinburgh: The Edinburgh College of Naturopathy, Osteopathy and Chiropractic; circa 1935.

65. Richards R. *The Progressive* 1931; 2 (2), 3.

66. Hancock EL. Report of the first ECU

meeting. *Brussels Chiropractor* 1932; 1 (12), 14.

67. Gillet H. 50 years ago. *Bulletin of the European Chiropractors' Union* 1982; 30 (1), 3-4.

68. Minutes of the European Chiropractic Union meetings of Saturday July the 2nd 1932 and Friday July the 8th 1932. *The European Chiropractor* 1932; 1 (1), 2-3.

69. *The European Chiropractor* 1932; 1 (1), 1.

70. Chiropractic code of ethics: as drawn up and adopted at the 3rd general meeting in Paris 1933. *The European Chiropractic Bulletin* 1933; 2 (1), 12-13.

71. Gillet HJ. Chiropractic in Europe: a summary of the existing conditions abroad. *The Chiropractic Journal* 1934; 3 (3), 6-7.

72. *The European Chiropractic Bulletin* 1935; 4 (1), 3.

73. *The European Chiropractic Bulletin* 1932; 1 (1), 1.

74. *The European Chiropractic Bulletin* 1933; 1 (3): Special Jail Supplement, 1-2

75. *The European Chiropractic Bulletin* 1933; 2 (4), 13.

76. *The European Chiropractic Bulletin* 1933; 3 (4), 12.

77. Beyeler WR. The fight for legal recognition in the Canton of Zurich, Switzerland. *The European Chiropractic Bulletin* 1940; 8 (4), 3-14.

78. Lorez E. Short summary of the book's contents. In: Anfänge der Chiropraktik in der Schweiz: History of Chiropractic in Switzerland. Basal: Morf and Company; 2003, pp. 220-232.

79. Bannister CER. Ballot returns. *The European Chiropractic Bulletin* 1937; 5 (5), 1.

80. *The European Chiropractic Bulletin* 1938; 7 (3), 1.

81. Bannister CER. The Presidential address. *The European Chiropractic Bulletin* 1939; 7 (7), 2-4.

82. *The European Chiropractic Bulletin* 1939; 8 (1), 1.

83. *The European Chiropractic Bulletin* 1940; 8 (3), 1-2.

84. *The European Chiropractic Bulletin* 1946; 8 (6), 1-2.

85. *The European Chiropractic Bulletin* 1947; 9 (5-6), 5.

86. Bannister CER. The Presidential address. *The European Chiropractic Bulletin* 1946; 8 (6), 3-4.

87. Weiant CW. Education for Europe. *The European Chiropractic Bulletin* 1948; 10 (6-7), 5-7.

88. Simonsen IH, Deltoff MN, Johansen KK & Petersen JN. Dansk kiropraktor kursus: an historical perspective and overview of the Danish Chiropractors' School. *Chiropractic History* 1989; 9 (2), 21-24.

89. Hviid MG. The Danish Chiropractic College. In: Chapman-Smith D, translating editor. History of Chiropractic in Denmark. Toronto: Danish Pro-Chiropractic Association; 1984, p. 10. [Original text published in Danish; 1975].

90. Palmer BJ. Letter to Arthur G Scofield, dated 28th October, 1947. Archives, Anglo-European College of Chiropractic.

91. *The European Chiropractic Bulletin* 1947; 9 (1-2), 2.

92. Harding S. Biographies: Dr Mary Walker, 1880-1958. In: McTimoney Chiropractic: The First Twenty-Five Years. Abingdon: McTimoney Chiropractic Association; 1997, pp. 123-124.

93. Big news: first chiropractic school in Europe. *The European Chiropractic Bulletin* 1949; June 15th, 1-4.

94. Bad news folks!!! *The European Chiropractic Bulletin* 1949; June 15th, 14.

95. *The European Chiropractic Bulletin* 1949; March 15th, 2.

96. British Chiropractors' Association Journal. *The European Chiropractic Bulletin* 1949; March 15th, 4-5.

97. *The European Chiropractic Bulletin* 1949; June 15th, 4-5.

98. *The European Chiropractic Bulletin* 1947; 9 (1-2), 15-16.

99. Wight DM. European Chiropractic Union Conference: Copenhagen, Denmark, June 3, 4 and 5. *British Chiropractors' Association Journal* 1951; 15 (1), 3-6.

100. *ECU Bulletin* 1959; 2 (4), 1.

101. Gaucher-Peslherbe P. The progressive making of a foremost chiropractic researcher: Fred Illi, from Geneva. *Journal of Manipulative and Physiological Therapeutics* 1996; 19 (3), 178-184.

102. Weiant CW. B.J. Palmer and the 'German issue': the crisis in postwar European chiropractic. *Chiropractic History* 1982; 2 (1), 41-44.

103. Gaucher-Peslherbe P. Chiropractic around the world. In: Peterson D & Wiese G, editors. Chiropractic: An Illustrated History. London: Mosby; 1995, p. 472.

104. *Bulletin of the European Chiropractic Union* 1961; 2 (2), 9.

105. Gjocih A. Chiropractic, as it was, as it is. *Bulletin of the European Chiropractic Union* 1961; 1 (6), 6.

106. Draux M. Palmerian philosophy. *Bulletin of the European Chiropractic Union* 1963; 3 (9), 1-2.

107. Rational chiropractic. *Bulletin of the European Chiropractic Union* 1963; 3 (9), 3-4.

108. *Annals of the Swiss Chiropractors' Association* 1960; 3.

109. Gillet H. Vertebral fixations, an introduction to movement palpation. *Annals of the Swiss Chiropractors' Association* 1960; 30-33.

110. Liekens M. Movement palpation. *Annals of the Swiss Chiropractors' Association* 1960; 34-42.

111. Danish D.C.s report student recruitment gains. *Bulletin of the European Chiropractic Union* 1963; 4 (6), 18-19.

112. Grillo F. The new Constitution of the E.C.U.

and the election of the Professional Council. *Bulletin of the European Chiropractors' Union* 1964; 5 (3), 11-13.

113. A new and better E.C.U. *Bulletin of the European Chiropractic Union* 1964; 4 (8), 11-14.

114. New Constitution. *Bulletin of the European Chiropractors' Union* 1965; 6 (7), 15.

115. Constitution of the European Chiropractors' Union. 1964. Archives, Anglo-European College of Chiropractic.

116. Secretary's report 1962. *Bulletin of the European Chiropractic Union* 1962; 2 (2), 5-7.

117. Report on the Swiss Chiropractors' Forum. *Bulletin of the European Chiropractic Union* 1963; 4 (6), 10-12.

118. Prospectus of the Anglo-European College of Chiropractice; 1968-1970. Archives, Anglo-European College of Chiropractic.

119. Anglo-European Chiropractic College takes shape. *Bulletin of the European Chiropractors' Union* 1964; 5 (3), 19.

120. Anglo-European College of Chiropractic Ltd: College report. *Bulletin of the European Chiropractors' Union* 1965; 6 (10), 3.

121. The A.E.C.C. is open! *Bulletin of the European Chiropractors' Union* 1965; 7 (4), 1.

122. Bennett D. Anglo-European College of Chiropractice. *Bulletin of the European Chiropractors' Union* 1965; 7 (6), 8-10.

123. Bennett D. Letter to Joseph Janse at National College of Chiropractic, dated 20th January, 1967. Archives, National College of Chiropractic.

124. Anglo-European College of Chiropractic. *Bulletin of the European Chiropractic Union* 1969; 18 (4), 22.

125. Harding S. John McTimoney: His life and vision. In: McTimoney Chiropractic: The First Twenty-Five Years. Abingdon: McTimoney Chiropractic Association; 1997, pp. 21-27.

126. Editorial. *Bulletin of the European Chiropractors Union* 1976; 24 (2), page unnumbered.

127. Christensen A. Letter to all European chiropractors, dated 10th July 1980. Archives, Anglo-European College of Chiropractic.

128. News from AECC. *Bulletin of the European Chiropractors Union* 1980; 28 (3), 8-9.

129. Editorial. *E.C.U. Bulletin* 1976; 24 (1), 1.

130. Editorial. *Bulletin of the European Chiropractors Union* 1980; 28 (4), 2.

131. Greenwood E. Attributes of a profession. *Social Work* 1957; 2 (3), 44-45.

132. Wilenski HL. The professionalization of everyone? *American Journal of Sociology* 1964; 70 (2), 137-158.

133. Programme for the European Chiropractors' Union Golden Jubilee Convention, 20th-23rd May 1982. Archives, Anglo-European College of Chiropractic.

134. Major cuts the tape! *AECC Newsletter* 1982; 2, 1-2.

135. Christensen A. Letter from the President. *European Journal of Chiropractic* 1984; 32 (3), 129-130.

136. Archambáult C. Editorial: the future developments of chiropractic education in France. *European Journal of Chiropractic* 1985; 33 (3), 141-142.

137. Kilvaer A. Chiropractic education: the European Council on Chiropractic Education (ECCE). *European Journal of Chiropractic* 1989; 37 (4), 125-128.

138. ECU research fund established. *European Journal of Chiropractic* 1982; 30 (3), 186-187.

139. Molloy R. Editorial: European Journal of Chiropractic – a change for the better. *European Journal of Chiropractic* 1982; 30 (2), 63.

140. Molloy R. Editorial: a recommendation for the formation of an Editorial Board. *European Journal of Chiropractic* 1982; 30 (3), 125.

141. Stokke Ø. Statistikk om Kiropraktikk. Tromsø: Scandinavian University Books; 1977.

142. Breen AC. Chiropractic in Britain. *Annals of the Swiss Chiropractors' Association* 1976; VI, 207-218.

143. Breen AC. Chiropractors and the treatment of back pain. *Rheumatology and Rehabilitation* 1977; 16, 46-53.

144. Christensen A. Letter from the President. *European Journal of Chiropractic* 1983; 31 (3), 1.

145. Report of a Working Group. Comparison of chiropractic and hospital outpatient management of low back pain: a feasibility study. *European Journal of Chiropractic* 1986; 34 (4), 172-181.

146. Meade TW, Dyer S, Browne W, Townsend J & Frank AO. Low back pain of mechanical origin: randomised comparison of chiropractic and hospital outpatient management. *British Medical Journal* 1990; 300 (6737), 1431-1437.

147. Correspondence: Low back pain: comparison of chiropractic and hospital outpatient treatment. *British Medical Journal* 1990; 300 (6740), 1647-1650.

148. Assendelft WJJ, Bouter LM & Kessels AGH. Effectiveness of chiropractic and physiotherapy in the treatment of low back pain: a critical discussion of the British randomised clinical trial. *Journal of Manipulative and Physiological Therapeutics* 1991; 14 (5), 281-286.

149. Breen A & Langworthy JM. The impact of the publication of the MRC trial on the economics of UK chiropractic practice: a questionnaire survey. *European Journal of Chiropractic* 1991; 39 (2), 59-63.

150. The World Chiropractic Congress. *Bulletin of the European Chiropractic Union* 1962; 2 (2), 14.

151. Diem C. President's message for 1989. *European Journal of Chiropractic* 1989; 37 (2), 33-35.

152. Jacobsen J. Reports from the National Associations. Chiropractic in Denmark: progressing in leaps and bounds. *European Journal of Chiropractic* 1990; 38 (4), 193-196.

153. Pedersen P. A survey of chiropractic practice in Europe. *European Journal of Chiropractic*

1994; 42 (1), 3-28.

154. Nilsson N. News from the Colleges. Anglo-European College of Chiropractic UK. Council for National Academic Awards. *European Journal of Chiropractic* 1988; 36 (2), 53.

155. Christensen A. News from the Colleges. AECC. *European Journal of Chiropractic* 1990; 38 (2), 87-88.

156. Humphreys BK & Bolton JE. European chiropractic education: development of Masters degree chiropractic education at the Anglo-European College of Chiropractic. *European Journal of Chiropractic* 1998; 46 (1), 23-26.

157. Accreditation of chiropractic degree programme at University of Southern Denmark – Odense. *Backspace* 1999; 4 (2), 1.

158. Morley J. European chiropractic education: development of Masters degree chiropractic education at the University of Surrey. *European Journal of Chiropractic* 1998; 46 (1), 27-28.

159. King S. University of Glamorgan introduces funded chiropractic degree. *Backspace* 1998; 3 (2), 9.

160. King S & Young KJ. The founding of the Welsh Institute of Chiropractic. *Chiropractic History* 2002; 22 (2), 25-30.

161. Evidence-based Medicine Working Group. Evidence-based medicine. A new approach to teaching the practice of medicine. *Journal of the American Medical Association* 1992; 268 (17), 2420-2425.

162. Sackett DL, Straus SE, Richardson WS, Rosenberg W & Haynes RB. Introduction. In: Evidence-based Medicine. How to Practice and Teach EBM. 2nd Edition. London: Churchill-Livingstone; 2000, pp. 1-12.

163. Agency for Health Care Policy and Research. Management Guidelines for Acute Low Back Pain. Rockville: Agency for Health Care Policy and Research, United States Department of Health and Human Services; 1994.

164. Clinical Standards Advisory Group. Report on Back Pain. London: Her Majesty's Stationery Office; 1994.

165. Royal College of General Practitioners. Clinical Guidelines for the Management of Acute Low Back Pain. London: Royal College of General Practitioners; 1996.

166. Koes BW, van Tulder MW, Ostelo R, Burton AK & Waddell G. Clinical guidelines for the management of low back pain in primary care: an international comparison. *Spine* 2001; 26 (22), 2504-2514.

167. Breen A. Evidence-based practice: friend or foe? *British Journal of Chiropractic* 1997; 1 (1), 2-3.

168. Ernst E & Assendelft WJJ. Chiropractic for low back pain: we don't know whether it does more good than harm. *British Medical Journal* 1998; 317 (7152), 160.

169. WFC 6th Biennial Congress – 20-28 May 2001 held in conjunction with the European Chiropractors' Union and the Association Française de Chiropratique. *Backspace* 2001;

unnumbered issue, 1.

170. Inauguration and graduation: Ivry-sur-Seine – 13th May 1999. *Backspace* 1999; 4 (1), 6-7.

171. The Paris Paradigm of Chiropractic. WFC members adopt ACC paradigm: what does it mean for you? *The Chiropractic Report* 2001; 15 (4), 1-3, 6-8.

172. WFC's consultation on the profession's identity. Why an agreed identity is vital, and your role. *The Chiropractic Report* 2004; 18 (1), 1-3, 6-8.

173. The spinal health care experts. The profession reaches agreement on identity. *The Chiropractic Report* 2005; 19 (4), 1.

174. World Federation of Chiropractic has a new President. *Backspace* 2004; unnumbered issue, 5.

175. World Health Organisation. WHO Guidelines on Basic Training and Safety in Chiropractic. Geneva: World Health Organisation; 2005.

176. Bunker V, Castle A, Mills G & Bolton JE. Professional doctorates in healthcare disciplines in the UK: a new professional doctorate in Chiropractic. *European Journal of Chiropractic* 2003; 48 (3), 107-109.

177. Vall K. AECC receives public funding. *Backspace* 2005; 1 (1), 14.

178. Chiropractic education. *Backspace* 2005; 1 (1), 1.

179. European Academy of Chiropractic. *Backspace* 2006; 2 (1), 1, 4.

180. UK BEAM Trial Team. United Kingdom back pain exercise and manipulation (UK BEAM) randomised trial: the effectiveness of physical treatments for back pain in primary care. *British Medical Journal* 2004; 329 (7479), 1377.

181. UK BEAM Trial Team. United Kingdom back pain exercise and manipulation (UK BEAM) randomised trial: cost effectiveness of physical treatments for back pain in primary care. *British Medical Journal* 2004; 329 (7479), 1381.

182. Dixon P. President's message. *Backspace* 2003; February, 1, 3.

183. Veggia G. Intrusion into our profession. Our worst enemies – chiropractors! *Backspace* 2005; 1 (1), 10.

184. White IE. A serious lack of loyalty. *Backspace* 2005; 1 (1), 11.

185. Dixon P. President's report. *Backspace* 2004; March, 1-2.

186. The chiropractic profession. *The Chiropractic Report* 2005; 19 (2), 1-8.

SECTION B

HISTORIES OF CHIROPRACTIC IN EUROPEAN NATIONS

1. CHIROPRACTIC IN BELGIUM

A short history of chiropractic in Belgium, by John Gillet

KEY FACTS: BELGIUM
Population: 10 million
National Chiropractic Association: Union Belge des Chiropractors
Number of chiropractors registered with National Association (October 2006): 96
President of National Association (October 2006): Pierre Mercier
Website: www.chiropraxie.org

The history of chiropractic in Belgium is, in the beginning, tightly linked to the Gillet family. It started with Jules Gillet, the first chiropractor in Belgium, who established his practice in Brussels in 1923. Jules was joined first by his eldest son Marcel in 1925 and then by Henri in 1928. The Gillet family were to become key players in the development of chiropractic in Europe, and indeed, as a result of their research, internationally recognised. Two other chiropractors came to Belgium in the 1920s. They were E D'Arras who settled in Antwerp in 1925, and H Poeck, who also practised in Antwerp from 1927.

Early on in their careers, Marcel and Henri Gillet made their presence known within the European chiropractic community. In 1931 they first published a bulletin, the *Brussels Chiropractor: News and Opinions*, sent free of charge to all known "chirobrothers" in Europe. In 1932, the Gillets were involved in the founding of the European Chiropractic Union (ECU) in London and shortly afterwards their publication, the *Brussels Chiropractor*, became the *European Chiropractor*, with Henri Gillet as Editor.

In 1932 Belgian chiropractors formed the Belgian Chiropractors' Association (BCA). In 1935 it played host to the European Chiropractic Union's annual convention, at the time of the World Fair in Brussels. During the convention, Dr E D'Arras was elected as

Figure 42. Chiropractors at the 1935 ECU Convention in Brussels

Vice President of the ECU and Dr Henri Gillet its Registrar. 1935 also saw the creation of a pro-chiropractic layperson's association in Belgium. Belgian chiropractors would go on to host ECU conventions in Ostend in 1963 and in Brussels in 1994. They would work with the Dutch in organising an ECU convention in Amsterdam in 1976.

In the years prior to World War II only a small number of chiropractors practised in Belgium. In 1939 there were only 11 chiropractors in the country. During the War, Marcel Gillet started researching the concept of the subluxation. He came to the conclusion that it was *stiffness*, *motion in-coordination*, *limitation in motion*, or *fixation* that were most important in

understanding the subluxation, and not misalignment as had been traditionally proposed and taught in chiropractic schools. The idea that a subluxation could be best understood as an abnormality of position (misalignment) was replaced by the idea that it could be best understood as an abnormality of movement. This led Marcel and his brother Henri to *motion palpation* as a means of assessing the function of joints. Later, the Gillets and Maurice Liekens, who joined them, developed a theory of *fixation complexes* and a notion of hypo- and hyper-mobility as consequences of the subluxation. Maurice Liekens also developed an apparatus to test sacro-iliac mobility.

Marcel Gillet was the first European

chiropractor to be named a fellow of the International College of Chiropractors. He was also approached by Dr Fred Illi in the late 1930s to become a teacher at a proposed European college which was to be situated in Geneva, Switzerland. It was anticipated that he might teach with Joseph Janse (USA), Ida Gerber (Switzerland), Clarence Wiant (USA), Willy Beyeler (Switzerland) and Fred Illi (Switzerland). In the event, the plans for a chiropractic school in Switzerland were abandoned with the outbreak of World War II. In the absence of a European college, Henri Gillet and Maurice Liekens created a students' loan fund just after the War, to lend young men and women money to study chiropractic in the USA. Students had to reimburse their loan to the fund when they started to practise, so as to help others after them.

In 1946 the Belgian Chiropractors' Association, *Association des Chiropraticiens Belges*, was officially recognised when its statutes were legally deposited. Henri Gillet was elected President of the Association. In 1951 he published the first edition of his *Belgian Chiropractic Association Research Notes*. During the 1950s the Association published the *Cahiers de l'ABC*, a series intended to inform patients about such things as chiropractic and its history, the nervous system and the vertebral column.

The socio-political environment in Belgium was never easy for the chiropractors practising there. Indeed, the Belgian system of law based on *Napoleonic Code* gave doctors of medicine

the sole rights to prescribe and treat, or to order different treatments for patients. Complaints from the established medical profession against chiropractors started in the 1920s. In 1927 Jules Gillet was found guilty of illegal practice of medicine, as later would be his sons. Dr E D'Arras went to court in 1929, but was acquitted.

The period between 1964 and 1997 saw a number of complaints against chiropractors from the Order of Medical Doctors, but with the help of their legal advisor Jacques Lemaire, chiropractors defended themselves successfully. 1977 saw a particularly large number of prosecutions, when, after a complaint from medical specialists, the offices of 28 chiropractors in Brussels and surrounding areas were raided simultaneously at 8 o'clock in the morning by police searching for proof of the illegal practice of medicine. Offices were sealed so that they could not be used; however, the prosecutions that followed were not successful in stopping chiropractors practising in the long term.

It was during the 1970s that the first major efforts to gain legal recognition for chiropractic in Belgium were made. Frank Van Eeckhoven, President of the BCA from 1962 until 1984, led the political campaign, with Jacques Lemaire as juridical counsellor and legal advisor. In 1976 there were round-table discussions with Belgian political and scientific authorities, but it would be more than 20 years before chiropractors would receive the statutory recognition that they sought.

Figure 43. Henri Gillet, pioneer of motion palpation

Michel Fossé succeeded Frank Van Eeckhoven as President of the BCA in 1984 and continued to apply political pressure for acceptance of chiropractic under law. During his presidency a trip was organised to take Belgian government representatives to the USA to show them a number of chiropractic colleges. The trip seemed a tremendous success at the time, but little action followed on the part of politicians. In 1990 another trip was organised, this time to the Anglo-European College of Chiropractic (AECC) in Great Britain, for a Belgian government official and a European Union representative. Although the efforts of Fossé and others to achieve statutory regulation for chiropractic in Belgium during the 1980s and early 1990s did not achieve their aim at the time, there was at least success in ensuring that chiropractic services were exempt from value added tax (VAT) in Belgium.

In 1994 a petition of patients was organised in support of legislation for chiropractic. In a period of three months some 213,000 signatures were collected, impressive in a country that had only 70 chiropractors in its national association. For the first time ever, chiropractic made front-page news in Belgium. By 1996, when Philippe Druart became President of the BCA, politicians were giving very serious thought to the demands of chiropractors and their patients. In July 1997, the Health Minister, Marcel Colla, invited chiropractors to a meeting in Brussels along with representatives of three other disciplines: homeopathy, acupuncture and osteopathy, to present his own project of law. In October 1997, the Health Minister organised a round-table meeting to which he invited the Royal Academies of Medicine, the medical unions, the medical university faculties, MPs of the Health Commission and representatives from the 4 "non-conventional medicines". Despite medical opposition, the government encouraged a movement towards legalisation of these disciplines. The framework for a new law was approved by the Chamber of Representatives on Thursday 22nd March 1999 and by the Senate soon afterwards. The final step in the legislative process, a Royal

Decree, is yet to be implemented. Since 2002, under Pierre Mercier's presidency of the BCA, the BCA has been working with politicians to finally establish what should and what should not be included in this legislation for chiropractic.

Today patients who go for treatment to chiropractors in Belgium may be eligible to receive partial refunds through social reimbursement sick-funds. Chiropractic is becoming increasingly understood and accepted within society and there are now nearly 100 chiropractors practising in Belgium. The current President of the ECU, Philippe Druart, is Belgian.

2. CHIROPRACTIC IN CYPRUS

A short history of chiropractic in Cyprus, by Efstathios (Stathis) Papadopoulos

KEY FACTS: CYPRUS
Population: <1 million
National Chiropractic Association: Sindesmos Chiropracton Kyprou
Number of chiropractors registered with National Association (October 2006): 10
President of National Association (October 2006): Efstathios (Stathis) Papadopoulos

Cyprus, Europe's easternmost Mediterranean island, lies at the crossroads of Europe, Asia and Africa. Even though it is a small country, it has a rich cultural heritage. Its importance has been recognised by the United Nations Educational, Scientific and Cultural Organisation (UNESCO), which has included 9 of the island's Byzantine mountain churches and the towns of Kato Pafos, Palaepafos and Choirokoitia on its World Cultural Heritage List. Following the Turkish invasion in 1974, a significant part of the Island, and much of its cultural wealth, has been under Turkish occupation.

The history of chiropractic in Cyprus begins with the arrival of Dr Dinos Ramon, a graduate of Palmer College, who set up his practice in his native town of Famaghusta in 1967. He was the first chiropractor on the Island. Due to his hard work and the therapeutic results he achieved, Dinos Ramon's practice flourished and by 1974 he was able to set up a large chiropractic health centre in Pogazi, by the beach, with a complex of 64 rooms for visiting patients. All his dreams came to an abrupt end with the Turkish occupation of the northern part of Cyprus, which included Famaghusta. As a refugee, with nothing in his pockets, he arrived in Limassol and set up practice in a tent at a refugee camp.

Ramon was the first President of the Cyprus

Figure 44. Phylactis Ierides (left), Dinos Ramon (centre), and Efstathios (Stathis) Papadopoulos (right), pioneer chiropractors in Cyprus, pictured at Dr Ramon's office after the passage of a chiropractic law in 1991

Chiropractic Association and along with Dr Efstathios (Stathis) Papadopoulos was instrumental in uniting chiropractors in Greece. He served as a President of the Ellenic Chiropractors' Association and today divides his time between Nicosia in Cyprus and Athens, Greece.

The second chiropractor to practise in Cyprus was Dr George Djiovannis, who arrived in 1977. Like Ramon, he was a graduate of Palmer College. He set up his practice in Larnaca, but in 1980 he was forced to return to the USA for family reasons.

Dr Phylactis Ierides was the third chiropractor to practise on the Island. He, like Djiovannis, arrived in 1977. A graduate of National College of Chiropractic, he set up in Lemesos, where he is still practising today. Apart from his chiropractic work, he is also a talented sculptor. Ierides was the first chiropractor in Cyprus to fall foul of Cypriot law, which did not recognise chiropractic. On 5th March 1985 the Cypriot Medical Association filed charges against Dr Ierides after he referred a patient to a medical doctor. He was accused of practising medicine without a licence. Following a series of court appearances, Ierides was found guilty under law, but the judge did not pass any penalty on him and recommended that a separate law should be created to cover chiropractors. This court case acted as a catalyst towards the statutory regulation of chiropractic in Cyprus. Dr Ierides is currently Vice President of the

Cyprus Chiropractic Association and ECU Convention Administrative Organiser.

I (Dr Efstathios Papadopoulos), a 1981 Palmer College graduate, was the fourth chiropractor to practise on the Island, but since Dr Djiovannis had returned to the United States, we numbered only 3 practitioners at the time of my arrival. I recall being welcomed with open arms by Dr Ramon and Dr Ierides in late 1982, when I came to set up my practice in Nicosia. I soon realised that despite the efforts of my colleagues, the profession was little known. Medical co-operation was non-existent. In fact we faced considerable hostility.

A meeting of chiropractors was called, and it was decided that we should get a lawyer to give advice about the formation of an association and also to help with the advancement of chiropractic in Cyprus. The Cyprus Chiropractic Association was formed in 1984 under the direction of a young lawyer, Andreas Georkadjis of Limassol, who in 1985 became the defence lawyer for Dr Ierides' court case.

In the years that followed the 3 pioneer chiropractors of Cyprus stood together in pursuit of the development of chiropractic and its regulation under law. At this point I can relate the following incident. It was decided that I would be in charge of the legislative effort, so I called the Ministry of Health for an appointment with the then Minister of Health, Dr Pelekanos who was a medical doctor. After trying to get an appointment for almost 6 months, I called the Minister's Private Secretary and asked her to convey verbatim the following message, "Either the Minister and his staff have too much to do, in which case they should ask for help, or they are totally incompetent, in which case they should all resign". The next morning at 9 o'clock the phone rang and I was given an appointment.

All 3 of the chiropractors practising in Cyprus turned up for the meeting with the Minister of Health and discussions began. At one point the Minister leaned forward and asked, "And how many are you?" The reply was "3", at which the Minister raised his voice and said to me: "And you have the audacity to waste my time?" I retorted, "No sir, we are giving you the chance to do something right from the beginning for our new profession". That is how we began the fight for legal regulation of chiropractic in Cyprus, a fight which lasted almost 8 years and saw several changes of Health Minister. Finally, on 22nd March 1991, the House of Representatives unanimously passed a Chiropractic bill into law.

In view of the difficulties faced by chiropractors in Cyprus in the years prior to 1991, I saw a need for international co-operation, and hence in 1987 I attended the Presidents' Summit which was held in London, which took the historic decision to form a World Federation of Chiropractic (WFC). The WFC came into being in 1988 in Australia. I was also one of the founding members of International Federation of Sports Chiropractic. Presently, I hold the following positions: President of the Cyprus Chiropractic Association, First Vice-President of the ECU, ECU Executive Representative to the European Council on Chiropractic Education, First Vice-President of the WFC, Member of the International Affairs Committee of the National Board of Chiropractic Examiners (USA), and advisor to the International Board of Chiropractic Examiners.

On 26th May 2003, at the request of World Health Organisation (WHO) officials, I was invited as the then Secretary-Treasurer of the WFC to address the WHO Assembly in Geneva, supporting a resolution in favour of greater regulation and incorporation of traditional, complementary and alternative medicines within healthcare. This was an historic event, as it was the first presentation to a WHO Assembly by a chiropractor. More recently, I have worked to separate European educational issues from ECU politics through the establishment of a European Academy of Chiropractic.

The fifth chiropractor to arrive in Cyprus came from Australia in 1991. He was Dr George Efstathiou, a graduate of Sydney University and Chiropractic College, who set up practice in Larnaca and his hometown Ormidia. He has a particular interest in sport and took part in the All African Games in Johannesburg and in the Mediterranean Games in Tunis. He presently heads the National Chiropractic Sports Council.

Since 1991 there has been a steady influx of chiropractors into Cyprus. The Cyprus Chiropractic Association currently has 10

Figure 45. Members of the ECU General Council in Lemesos, 2005

members. In recent years the country has played host to 2 important meetings of chiropractors. In 1996 the WFC held a meeting of its Council in Lefkosia. In 2005 chiropractors of the ECU gathered for their annual convention in Lemesos. In 2007 another important meeting is planned in Lemesos, to be hosted by the Cyprus Chiropractic Association, with the aim of furthering organisation and promotion of chiropractic in the eastern Mediterranean region.

3. CHIROPRACTIC IN DENMARK

A short history of chiropractic in Denmark, by Søren Bak-Jensen

KEY FACTS: DENMARK
Population: 5 million
National Chiropractic Association: Dansk Kiropraktor-Forening
Number of chiropractors registered with National Association (October 2006): 538
President of National Association (October 2006): Peter Kryger-Baggesen
Website: www.kiropraktor-foreningen.dk

Since its beginning in the years following World War I, Danish chiropractic has gone from a position of outsider to an established position in the healthcare field. This has been brought about by greater acceptance from the medical profession, but also through a change of attitude from the chiropractors themselves. Danish chiropractors have moved from trying to present an alternative to medical science, towards working in cooperation with other healthcare professions, especially medical doctors.

The first chiropractic clinic in Denmark was opened in Copenhagen in 1920 by Sofus Larsen, an electro-engineer and 1919 graduate of the Palmer School of Chiropractic. Other clinics opened in the major provincial towns during the early 1920s, and in 1925 the 11 chiropractors practising in Denmark at the time founded the Danish Chiropractors' Association (DCA). The Association established contacts with chiropractors in other countries, and Danish chiropractors were closely involved in the establishment of the ECU in 1931. During the 1930s, the number of Danish chiropractors grew steadily, reaching 50 in 1940. This meant that Denmark had the highest number of chiropractors per capita of any European country during the interwar years.

The earliest practitioners of chiropractic in Denmark were only allowed to treat patients who had been referred to them by a medical doctor. The Danish Medical Association excluded any member who cooperated with chiropractic clinics, forcing chiropractors to

Figure 46. Svend Buaas, a Danish chiropractor who trained at the Palmer School of Chiropractic, pictured in his clinic, circa 1935

start of a period of stagnation and decline for the chiropractic profession in Denmark. Several older chiropractors resigned, and restrictions on cross-Atlantic travel meant that new ones did not arrive from North America. In order to alleviate this problem, the DCA decided to establish a school of their own. The Association set up strict standards of entry to the course. Fifteen students were accepted, and teaching began in autumn 1948. The students received their basic medical and scientific training by attending lectures at the medical faculty of the University of Copenhagen. Parallel to this, they were taught chiropractic diagnostics and technique at a chiropractic clinic. The students graduated in 1951 after $3\frac{1}{2}$ years of study.

This generation of chiropractors led the way towards a new era in Danish chiropractic that would profoundly change the status of this healing method. The younger chiropractors were highly critical of earlier chiropractic theories and education and wanted to base their practice on a more conventional scientific basis. This meant that the DCA gradually departed from their confrontational course towards medical doctors, despite the fact that chiropractors were still subject to attacks from the medical profession. This new strategy proved successful in bringing the chiropractors closer to formal recognition. During the 1960s, a governmental committee, which included chiropractors, discussed how chiropractic might become part of the public healthcare system. Central to discussions was the demand from chiropractors that all

rely on the services of a few renegade medical doctors. Therefore, the DCA launched a series of applications to the Danish state for better conditions of practice, primarily through state authorisation of chiropractors as well as inclusion in public health insurance schemes. The chiropractors' image as effective, low-tech, and no-nonsense healers won them both political and popular support, most clearly expressed through a petition delivered to the Danish government in 1941 carrying the signatures of almost 104,000 persons demanding that the DCA's demands were met. Still, the chiropractors and their supporters were not able to swing the political majority, and the application was turned down.

The outbreak of World War II marked the

chiropractic patients should be eligible for public healthcare support. The medical profession demanded that this should be the case only for patients referred to the chiropractor by a medical doctor. Professional independence had been a central element in chiropractors' demands for recognition since the 1920s, and when the Danish government decided to make public health remuneration dependent upon medical referral, the DCA refused to cooperate. Yet by the late 1970s, the chiropractors were gaining strong political and popular support, and in 1978 the demand for medical referral was lifted. In 1992, a state authorisation scheme for chiropractors was introduced in Denmark. And in 1994, as a truly remarkable event in the history of chiropractic worldwide, a publicly financed institute of chiropractic was set up at the University of Odense in southern Denmark offering a 5-year course. This course is now responsible for training the new chiropractors in Denmark.

There are now more than 500 authorised chiropractors in Denmark, a high number for

Figure 47. European chiropractors in Copenhagen, 1954

such a small country. Remuneration from public health insurance has been gradually extended over the years, and chiropractors are now accepted as filling an important niche within the range of healthcare services. In that way, the chiropractor of today is very different from the chiropractor of the interwar period, who claimed to offer a completely new understanding of disease, one that would eventually replace medical science. While few modern chiropractors long for a return to the days when chiropractors were generally regarded as the worst kind of quacks, some fear that chiropractors may have sacrificed too much of their identity in the attempt to win legitimacy in the eyes of healthcare authorities. The future for Danish chiropractors may prove to be a balancing act between conforming to general scientific principles of research and therapy and maintaining a distinct profile.

4. CHIROPRACTIC IN FINLAND

A short history of chiropractic in Finland, by Tuomo Ahola

KEY FACTS: FINLAND
Population: 5 million
National Chiropractic Association: Suomen Kiropraktikkoliitto r.y.
Number of chiropractors registered with National Association (October 2006): 44
President of National Association (October 2006): Stefan Malmqvist
Website: www.kiropraktiikka.org

The first Finnish chiropractor, Tauno Immanuel Kokko, graduated 5th May 1927 from the Pacific Chiropractic College in Portland, Oregon, USA. He was born on 26th March 1908 in Viipuri, Finland. He became an orphan at the age of 11, and was taken care of by his aunt. Eventually they moved to Vancouver in Canada. Tauno wanted to become a priest, but his North American relatives did not approve of the idea. They sent him to the Pacific Chiropractic College in Portland, a city where his uncle Peter Kokko had a large chiropractic clinic. After his graduation Kokko worked mainly in the USA, but occasionally visited Finland. According to his son and wife, Kokko designed field hospitals for the Finnish Army during World War II. After the War, Kokko returned to the USA and undertook post-graduate studies at Western States Chiropractic College. Due to visa and working permission problems he returned to Finland in 1951. He set up practice in Törnävä, in the province of Ostrobothia, because that was an area from which many immigrants to America had migrated. Because of this strong link to the USA, Ostrobothians were more aware of chiropractic than those in other parts of Finland. Tauno Kokko moved to Helsinki 1956 with his wife, Alli-Liisa, and son, Yrjö. He felt professionally isolated and became a member of the ECU on 14th July 1955. According to his wife he often travelled to seminars abroad, and some certificates of these trips remain in the Finnish Chiropractic Union (FCU) archives. He generally had a good relationship with the medical profession. Many medical doctors were Kokko's patients. Kokko did not approve of the folk healers visiting his practice. He felt they were trying to learn from him, rather than going abroad to study a whole degree. Tauno Kokko became the first honorary member of the FCU in 1982. He died on 27th December 1990.

The other Finnish chiropractic pioneer, Konstant Koski, took a totally different attitude and taught folk healers manual techniques. He was born on 3rd September 1896 in Kaustinen, Finland, and moved to the USA in 1913. Eventually he studied chiropractic and graduated in 1953 at the age of 57 from the National College of Chiropractic, in Chicago, Illinois. He had been a practitioner of manual therapy for 3 decades before his graduation as a chiropractor! Maybe that is why he chose to teach his skills to the bonesetters in Kaustinen. He did not teach manipulation, but he did teach mobilisation techniques. Today there is a large Folk Medicine Centre in Kaustinen, where a popular treatment is bonesetting, influenced by Koski. Konstant Koski died in November 1977 in Iron River, Michigan, USA.

Neither one of the two early pioneers of Finnish chiropractic sent students to follow in

Figure 48. Tauno Kokko, the first chiropractor to practise in Finland, pictured here at the time of his graduation as a chiropractor in 1927

their footsteps and study chiropractic. Instead, it needed a woman to give birth to the profession in Finland. Marjaleena Mäkinen was born on 1st July 1940 in Pori, Finland. She suffered from bad asthma and travelled to Norway hoping that the moist weather and a mountain hospital would help her condition. They did not, but Norwegian chiropractors did. Mäkinen was so happy that she decided to study chiropractic herself. She graduated from the Palmer College of Chiropractic on 29th March 1968. When she came back to Finland

Figure 49. Chiropractors on the First Biennial ChiroCruise organised by the Finnish Chiropractic Union (FCU) and the Swedish Chiropractic Association (SCA) in 2003. From left to right: Marion and Charles Masarsky (lecturer), Tuomo Ahola (FCU President), Stefan Malmqvist (SCA President), and Dr. Adrian Wenban (lecturer). After moving to Finland, Stefan Malmqvist became FCU President in January 2006.

civil servants from the National Board of Health (NBH) told her that she could not practise in Finland. They recommended she go back to the USA, or study for a qualification in massage. Mäkinen hired a lawyer, who although initially sceptical, used occupational legislation that allows every Finn to practise in the occupation they have studied a degree for, as a basis for defending her position. Mäkinen opened her practice on 12th May 1969 in Pori. She had changed her name from Marjaleena to Ragna and bought herself some used x-ray equipment. Surprisingly the NBH gave her permission to use it. However, in April 1970 a provincial medical officer threatened to stop her radiographic activity, but an appeal was accepted. Mäkinen's practice is still in the same premises and it is the oldest chiropractic clinic in Finland. She still takes radiographs there together with her son, Jaakko, who is the first second generation chiropractor in Finland.

Heikki Vähälä and Lasse Lappalainen were the first male nurses in Finland. Working as a medical agent in 1971, Vähälä heard an interview with Mäkinen on the radio. After visiting her on a number of occasions, Vähälä and Lappalainen left to study chiropractic in Davenport, Iowa, along with Vähälä's wife Terttu and a friend Markku Laaksonen. They were able to convince the NBH of the value of their educational plans and received student grants and loans from the Finnish state to study chiropractic. They graduated in 1976-7 and opened practices in Lahti, Finland. They did not have the problems that Mäkinen had had 8 years earlier. Medical attitudes towards these new chiropractors were variable. Some did not co-operate with them, whilst others came to them as patients.

Mäkinen (married name: Valli) and her 4 new colleagues founded the Finnish Chiropractic Association (which later became the Finnish Chiropractic Union) on 2nd November 1977. The Association was founded with the aims of achieving improved regulation for chiropractic in Finland, title protection, and state funding of fees. In the beginning the Association had neither the financial resources, nor the manpower to effectively pursue its aims. Terttu Vähälä and Markku Laaksonen ceased working as chiropractors and only 3 new members came to replace them during the next 8 years. Since then the membership of the Finnish Chiropractic Union (FCU) has increased by an average of 2 new members each year.

In the 1980s chiropractic became regulated under law in all the other Nordic countries and the title chiropractor was added into the Nordic agreement for healthcare professions. This decision forced the Finnish civil servants and politicians to register chiropractors in Finland as well. Originally chiropractic was the only manual profession that was supposed to be legally registered, however when legislation was passed in 1994 a number of other professions were registered including osteopaths and naprapaths. Chiropractors were registered with the title *koulutettu kiropraktikko*, trained chiropractor. That meant that anyone could still use the common title chiropractor, however, trained chiropractors became exempt from VAT and were given access to low price patient insurance (25 Euros in 2005). Trained chiropractors came under supervision of the National Bureau of Medico-Legal Affairs and provincial administrative boards.

For the last 10 years the FCU has tried to improve the legislative environment in which chiropractors work in Finland, but without success. However, during this period the Union has become more professionally managed. Fees have been raised and the financial resources of the Union have more than tripled during the last decade. The FCU has hired an administrator, developed a strategic plan for action 2005-2012, and the membership has been divided into working parties. There is a research group that is supervised by Professor Charlotte Leboeuf-Yde from the University of Southern Denmark. The FCU has also been accepted into the Tule ry, an umbrella organisation for organisations involved with musculoskeletal diseases (associated with the Bone and Joint Decade). Because of their movement towards professionalisation, chiropractors have generally earned better acceptance with the public and other healthcare professions. Trained chiropractors seem to have been able to positively differentiate themselves from the other manual professions in Finland. Court cases against lay chiropractors have helped in this differentiation, and the FCU has set appointments with civil servants with the aim of limiting the use of the title chiropractor to chiropractors who have graduated from a European Council on Chiropractic Education (ECCE) recognised institution.

5. CHIROPRACTIC IN FRANCE

A short history of chiropractic in France, by Benoit Rouy

KEY FACTS: FRANCE
Population: 64 million
National Chiropractic Association: Association Française de Chiropratique
Number of chiropractors registered with National Association (October 2006): 215
President of National Association (October 2006): Philippe Fleuriau

---

In 1905 Elizabeth Van Raders corresponded from Nice with DD Palmer, and subsequently travelled from France to the United States to study chiropractic. Although there is evidence that she revisited France after her graduation as a chiropractor, no evidence has come to light to show that she practised there. It is known that she practised chiropractic in the United States.

From available French sources, it appears that the first chiropractor to set up practice in France was Edward-Henry Schwing, in 1920. His family was originally from Alsace, but after the war of 1870 they emigrated from France to the United States, and that is where Edward-Henry was born. Having grown up in the United States, and having completed studies in medicine, he was drafted into the Medical Service in support of the military effort of World War I. He found himself in France in 1917. From there he had to be repatriated to the United States with a very severe case of tuberculosis. Finding medical treatments unsuccessful, his father, in desperation, insisted that he consult a chiropractor, the name of whom, history has unfortunately forgotten. A few weeks later, and to his deep surprise, he had fully recovered. He enrolled at once at the Palmer School of Chiropractic in Davenport.

After qualifying, Schwing returned to France and set up his practice in Paris, a city where *la Chiropratique* was generally unknown. His practice was successful, however he found himself at odds with the Parisian medical authorities of the day. When BJ Palmer visited Paris in 1925 he and his wife acted as tourist guides for them. In 1937 he published a book about chiropractic, *La chute d'Esculape*.

An immediate contender for the title of the first chiropractor to set up practice in France is Gaston-Lucien Gross, who was also from Alsace, and who graduated from the New York Chiropractic College in 1920. For many years Gross had the unfortunate honour of being the most persecuted chiropractor in France. Between 1920 and 1950 he was prosecuted more than 15 times, accused of illegally practising medicine by the French Medical Association. Only Charles Cligny from Troyes would challenge this record. He could not remember how many trials he had been through! Despite his troubles with the medical authorities, Gaston Gross carried on practising until the age of 93.

In 1951 the *Bulletin of the Association des Amis de la Chiropratique* referred to 12 chiropractors practising on French soil, although there may actually have been a few more. They used to be called the *12 apostles* and were: Max Brunner, Vincent Carnevale, Bernard Daudier, Thérèse Firstoss, Gaston Gross, Armand Manasson, René Morand, Georges Quinsier, Joseph Reveillard, Henri Schmoukler, J Schwab and Edward Schwing.

Most of these early pioneers graduated from the Palmer School of Chiropractic, but in the

Figure 50. Institut Franco-Européen de Chiropratique (IFEC), Paris

1960s and the 1970s a lot of the French chiropractors obtained their diplomas from other North American chiropractic institutions, principally: National College of Chiropractic, Cleveland Chiropractic College, New York Chiropractic College, Logan College of Chiropractic, Sherman College of Straight Chiropractic, and Canadian Memorial College of Chiropractic. Later there would be graduates from over the channel, from the Anglo-European College of Chiropractic. Then in 1984 the Institut Franco-Européen de Chiropratique (IFEC), in Ivry-sur-Seine near Paris, opened its doors. Nowadays the vast majority of prospective French chiropractors enrol to study chiropractic in France.

It has been more than a century since the French discovered *la Chiropratique*, however, despite increasing organisation of the chiropractic profession in France, and despite the existence of a chiropractic school in France recognised by the international chiropractic community, French chiropractors have not obtained the legal status that they believe they deserve. On the contrary, many of them have had to endure multiple legal persecutions. Between 1976 and 2001 the author has recorded 116 trials relating to accusations of illegal practice of medicine against chiropractors.

Since 1950 there have been a number of occasions where chiropractic has been discussed within the French Parliament. In 1953, the Minister of Education, André Marie, enacted a decree to organise the teaching of chiropractic at medical schools. It stated that where it was possible to find the necessary staff, the appointed professor would surround himself with one or several specialised persons (medical or non-medical), who, under his direction, would participate in teaching. It seems that the medical authorities never intended to appoint the only persons who might be seen to be competent to teach chiropractic, the chiropractors themselves. There the matter rested for some time. Then on 6th January 1962 there was another decree, which defined chiropractic to be solely a medical act. With this decree went the hopes

Figure 51. Students and staff of the Institut Franco-Européen de Chiropratique (IFEC)

of a generation of chiropractors in France for legal recognition of their profession in the short term.

It would be 40 years before hopes were once again raised. Contrary to all expectations, on 4th March 2002, under the initiative of the Minister of Health, Bernard Kouchner, the French Parliament adopted a law called: *Droit des Malades* (Sick Peoples' Rights), in which article 75 stated that professional use of the title "osteopath" or "chiropractor" is reserved for people who hold a diploma which has been granted by an institution approved by the Minister of Health, under conditions specified by a future decree. As of October 2006, we are still waiting for the publication of the long awaited decree. Given the power of the medical lobby in France and previous experience of laws pertaining to chiropractic, there is an air of scepticism within chiropractic ranks. As we say in France, we wait to find *à quelle sauce ils seront mangés* (with which sauce we will be eaten).

6. CHIROPRACTIC IN GERMANY

A short history of chiropractic in Germany, by Ingrid E White

KEY FACTS: GERMANY
Population: 82 million
National Chiropractic Association: Deutsche Chiropraktoren Gesellschaft e.V.
Number of chiropractors registered with National Association (October 2006): 63
President of National Association (October 2006): Michael Hafer

Manual therapies have been part of treatment regimes and evident in medical literature in central Europe for a long time. Descriptions of manipulation, similar to osteopathic and chiropractic manipulations, are to be found as early as 1718 in Professor Laurentius Heister's book, *Chirurgie* (Surgery), and in 1734 in Dr Johannes Storch's book, *Soldatenkrankheiten* (Soldiers' diseases).

Chiropractors came to set up practice in Germany in the 1920s. Evidence of the earliest Palmer School educated chiropractors to settle in Germany comes from Werner Peper's recollections, in his book, *Der Chiropraktische Report* (1978). The first were Alois L Jester in Frankfurt/Main in 1924, then Müller in Berlin, and Kurt Stein in Dresden in 1928. Peper was himself a Palmer graduate of 1933, and settled in Hamburg.

In the early 1950s Peper, according to his recollections, tried to interest Palmer College of Chiropractic in opening an affiliated school in Germany, but received the answer that there was only one "Chiropractic Fountain

Figure 52. Markus Fechler, responsible for organising the 2003 ECU Convention in Heidelberg (left); Ingrid White, President of the German Chiropractors' Association at the time (centre); and Michael Hafer (right)
(Courtesy of Barry Lewis, DC)

Head". He then attempted to interest both Palmer College and National College of Chiropractic in the United States in co-financing advertisements to attract young people from Germany to study chiropractic in the USA, but again was unsuccessful. Peper, disappointed by the lack of support and empathy, started to cooperate with medical doctors and later with lay healthcare practitioners by teaching them chiropractic techniques. So great was the interest of certain medical groups that BJ Palmer was invited to speak in Germany by Dr Gutmann of the *Physicians' Research and Clinical Association for Chiropractic* (FAC). Later this Association merged with another manual therapy group and became the medical association *Deutsche Gesellschaft für Manuelle Medizin* (DGMM), which actively promotes "chirotherapy" to this day. As it transpired, Palmer did not come to Germany. One of the probable reasons for this being opposition from Swiss and Scandinavian chiropractors who were concerned about chiropractic techniques falling into the hands of medical doctors. Peper eventually became disillusioned with the medical and lay medical groups, and as these groups became more knowledgeable in spinal manipulation, they seemed to forget where their knowledge and skills originated. He was also saddened by the fact that prominent chiropractors in Europe had started to call him the Judas of chiropractic in Germany. His work was, at least, recognised in a eulogy printed in *Manuelle Medizin* by one of the prominent medical chirotherapists who acknowledged Peper's involvement in the development of manual medicine in Germany.

In 1978, Werner Peper invited all the chiropractors he could find in Germany to meet in Hamburg. At this meeting, which was also attended by the then ECU President, Arne Christensen, those present decided to establish an association of German chiropractors. The Association was chartered and registered in Bremen in April 1980 by 9 founding members, namely: Theo Erlenbach (Mannheim), Hans J Häger (Bremen), Fritz Hartig (Oldenburg), Claus-Peter Hoff (Hamburg), Volkhart Homann (Peine), Hans Ihmsen (Hannover), Adelbert Lechler (Stuttgart) Ingrid Lisiecki (now White, Kaiserslautern), and Lothar Nafziger (Aachen). The German name for the Association was *Verband Graduierter Chiropraktoren Deutschlands e.V.* Since its inception, the Presidents of the Association have been Häger (1980-1984), Hübschmann (1984-1995), Fechler (1995-2000), White (2000-2004), and the current

Figure 53. From left to right looking at the camera: Joyce Miller, Michael Hafer and Douglas Hammond at the 2003 ECU Convention in Heidelberg
(Courtesy of Barry Lewis, DC)

President is Hafer. The Association now counts 63 members. In 2004 its name was changed to *Deutsche Chiropraktoren Gesellschaft* (DCG), which directly translates as: German Chiropractors' Association.

Two different laws regulate the registration and licensing of primary healthcare providers in Germany. One covers traditional medicine, its specialties and assistant professions. The second law, the lay medical practitioner statute (Heilpraktikergesetz), regulates licensure and scope of practice of all other independently working healthcare providers. Officially they are recognised as lay medical practitioners (Heilpraktiker). Chiropractors, no matter how highly educated, need to obtain the license as a lay medical practitioner if they want to pursue their profession legally, unless they are also medical physicians. The goal of the DCG is to establish a profession with a separate identity, a profession which is founded on full-time university-level education. This is not easy, because chiropractic in Germany was launched

into a kind of professional twilight zone between naturopathy and allopathic medicine, by being perceived as a technique, or set of techniques, utilised by different groups from pre-existing professions. In the past 20 to 25 years more and more chiropractors have come, mainly from the USA, to train non-chiropractors in chiropractic techniques on weekend courses. The DCG are concerned about the implications of this for patient safety, and also for chiropractic as a distinct and independent healthcare profession in Germany.

In order to establish chiropractic as a unique and separate profession, the DCG wish to insist on a minimum of 5 years university-level education for those wishing to practise chiropractic in Germany. They wish to accept the rigours of following European Council on Chiropractic Education (ECCE) standards, discourage the selling of chiropractic techniques by chiropractors to non-chiropractors, and work with the rest of the chiropractic profession in Europe to clarify a common identity for chiropractic. There is no shortcut to be had. It will be hard work, discipline and professionalism which will get us there – nothing short of that. The German Chiropractors' Association is well aware that there are hard choices to be made. It deliberately upholds international standards in chiropractic, instead of trying to embrace an uncontrollable situation by accepting members of different and/or substandard educational background.

7. CHIROPRACTIC IN GREAT BRITAIN

A short history of chiropractic in Great Britain, by Francis Wilson

---

KEY FACTS: GREAT BRITAIN
Population: 60 million
National Chiropractic Association: British Chiropractic Association
Number of chiropractors registered with National Association (October 2006): 1,284
President of National Association (October 2006): Barry Lewis
Website: www.chiropractic-uk.co.uk

Godfrey PM Heathcote was probably the first British national to study chiropractic, but he was not the first to travel from Britain to the United States with that specific aim. Heathcote had been resident in the United States for some 14 years when he made the decision to go to the Palmer School of Chiropractic in Davenport, Iowa, to study chiropractic in 1906. The first person to travel from Britain to study at the Palmer School was almost certainly Arthur D Eteson, who left Liverpool on 22nd October 1907. An article in the *Davenport Democrat and Leader* marked his arrival:

"An English student travels 4,500 miles to study at the Palmer School.

Chiropractic's Fountain Head, 828 Brady Street, Davenport, lays claim to the distinction of being the only school of its kind in America to which an English citizen has especially journeyed to study. The gentleman who has come to Davenport for that purpose is Arthur D. Eteson of Southport, England, who for many years has studied and practiced various reformed and rational methods of

healing, in the old country."
(Reported in: *The Chiropractor* 1907; 3 (12), 13)

Following his graduation as a chiropractor, it seems that Eteson returned to Southport. In the years that followed, others made the journey from Britain to the United States to study chiropractic. No doubt the cost would have been prohibitive for some, and those that did make the journey would either have had to have been well off, or prepared to make significant financial sacrifice. One of the more prestigious persons to attend the Palmer School in the years before World War I was Lord Charles Kennedy, who travelled to the School from Scotland. On 26th July 1911 the *Davenport Daily Times* reported:

"The Right Honourable lord Charles Kennedy, a Scotch peer, enrolled as a student at The Palmer School of Chiropractic, yesterday. He came all the way from Scotland to study at the Palmer School, showing his faith in the institution.

Lord Kennedy is stopping at the Kimball Hotel, and has his own automobile, which

Figure 54. Ben Bolt, the first President of the BCA, 1925-1929
Left: Ben Bolt, photographed in jail for practising medicine without a licence in California, before he returned to Britain in
1921. Right: Ben Bolt pictured in August 1960.

he brought with him from Scotland, and which he is using here."

(Extract from: *The Chiropractor* 1911; 7 (8), 3)

The number of those who made the journey from Britain to the United States to study chiropractic was not large. In 1920 the chiropractor Charles Bannister noted that there were only 6 chiropractors in England and one in Ireland. Having said this, in the absence of specific legislation, the distinction between who was, and who was not a chiropractor was not clear-cut. British Common Law permitted anyone to use the title *chiropractor* and practise *chiropractic*.

Despite their small numbers, those chiropractors that there were, began to organise themselves during the 1920s. Probably the first association of chiropractors in Britain was the Chiropractors' Association of the British Isles

which held its first meeting in Belfast in 1922. This was not a long-lasting association, but the British Chiropractors' Association (BCA), which was formed in 1925, was, and in time it came to represent the chiropractic mainstream of the United Kingdom.

The formation of the BCA was almost certainly in part a reaction to competition from osteopaths who were more numerous and better organised than chiropractors practising in Britain at the time. The BCA began with fewer than 20 members, but despite this an insurance scheme was soon set up for its members, and a code of ethics was also drawn up. At the 6th Annual Conference of the BCA in May 1931, ideas for the establishment of a pan-European organisation, a European Chiropractic Union, were discussed at an informal meeting after dinner. This discussion led to the formation of the ECU.

Figure 55. Members of the British Chiropractors' Association with BJ Palmer at a Conference in London, May 1934

In the years prior to the Second World War the BCA stood for *straight chiropractic*, palpation and adjustment (manipulation) of the joints of the human spinal column by hand only. Those chiropractors who would not abide by the principles of straight chiropractic were unwelcome within the Association.

By 1939 there were 75 chiropractors registered with the BCA, but the War years stifled chiropractic's development in Britain and the membership of the BCA fell to 35 by 1945. A particular problem during the War, and in the years immediately following it, was that potential students of chiropractic were unable to travel from Britain to the United States to study chiropractic and were also unable to transfer funds from Britain to the United States. The result was a lack of new blood entering the BCA. Following the War, the policy of the BCA to accept only those who agreed to practise straight chiropractic was relaxed as the Association was forced to adapt to survive.

The number of chiropractors practising in Britain remained low until the establishment of the first successful school in the country, the Anglo-European College of Chiropractic, which opened its doors to students in September 1965.

The period since 1965 has been one of rapid change for chiropractic in the United Kingdom, a period of growth and professionalisation. The number of chiropractors practising in the country has risen dramatically, as new schools have come into being, and relationships with the university sector have evolved. The first chiropractic undergraduate degree programme to be offered at a publicly funded British university was set up in 1997 at the University of Glamorgan in Wales.

Since 1965 educational standards have improved and clinical research has become an increasing priority as chiropractors have faced the challenges of evidence-based healthcare. Growing public knowledge and acceptance of chiropractic have aided in its development. Increasingly the medical profession, which for a long time merely tolerated the practice of chiropractic, has come to recognise value in chiropractic. Although the majority of patients who consult chiropractors in the United Kingdom today do so on a private basis, there has been some inclusion of chiropractic services within the country's National Health Service.

Arguably the most important event in chiropractic's recent socio-political development in the United Kingdom has been the passing of the Chiropractors Act in 1994, which resulted in protection of the title chiropractor. Today no-one can legally claim to be a chiropractor, or to practise chiropractic in the UK, unless they are registered with the statutory body, the General Chiropractic Council.

The United Kingdom currently has more chiropractors than any other single European nation. It is the only nation in Europe with more than one chiropractic school providing undergraduate education and training recognised by the European Council on Chiropractic Education (ECCE). The Anglo-European College of Chiropractic and the University of Glamorgan both hold accredited status with the ECCE, an organisation that strives to ensure that high standards of education are maintained within the European chiropractic community. The McTimoney College of Chiropractic, whilst offering a qualification in chiropractic recognised by Britain's General Chiropractic Council, has not been accredited by the ECCE and therefore cannot participate in ECU affairs. The title chiropractor is protected under British Law, but scope of practice is not defined in law. In October 2006 there were approximately 2,300 chiropractors registered with the General Chiropractic Council, most of whom were members of the BCA, the nation's longest established and largest association of chiropractors. The BCA represents the United Kingdom within the ECU and also within the World Federation of Chiropractic, of which it was a founding member. Other associations of chiropractors in the United Kingdom are the McTimoney Chiropractic Association (MCA), the Scottish Chiropractic Association (SCA) and the United Chiropractic Association (UCA). There is also a Chiropractic Patients' Association, which is linked with ProChiropractic Europe, a pan-European patients' association. In Britain, as in so many other European countries, chiropractic would not be where it is without the support of patients.

8. CHIROPRACTIC IN GREECE

A short history of chiropractic in Greece, by Vasileios Gkolfinopoulos

KEY FACTS: GREECE
Population: 11 million
National Chiropractic Association: Hellenic Chiropractors' Association
Number of chiropractors registered with National Association (October 2006): 25
President of National Association (October 2006): Vasileios Gkolfinopoulos
Website: www.chiropractic.gr

The Greek language holds the honour, as with many other medical and scientific terms, of naming chiropractic; chiro (χειρ-hand), practic (πράττω-doing), meaning done by hand. The ancient origins of chiropractic can be traced back to the time of Hippocrates, Asclepius and Galen. The *Book of Joints* by Hippocrates describes therapeutic procedures that seem to be based on a similar theoretical basis to chiropractic. Also, there exist ancient marble depictions of Asclepius performing what appears to be manipulative therapy of the neck.

The first chiropractor to practise in Greece was Kleanthis Ligeros, MD, PhD, DC, who set up his practice in 1924. He arrived at a time when the country was recovering from the Balkan Wars (1912-1913), World War I (1914-1918) and the Asia Minor catastrophe (1922), and was under a government formed by the Liberal Party leader Eleftherios Venizelos. It was a time of social unrest and political instability. Dr Ligeros studied DD Palmer's writings and became widely known for several books that he himself wrote, the most important of which are probably, *Rachialtherapy*, and *Chiropractic, the New Therapeutic Science*. His work concentrated on the association between ancient Greek therapeutics and chiropractic. He concluded that Palmer, being a scholar, must have based the formulation of his theory on the teachings of the ancient healers.

Dr Ligeros was followed by other Greek pioneers of chiropractic, whose names include Dr Moutsios (1928), Dr Mavroudis (1932) and Dr Chronis (1957). They practised and also produced written work on chiropractic, and on general health and well-being. They made efforts to achieve legislation for chiropractic in Greece, but were unsuccessful.

The first ever association to represent chiropractic in Greece was formed following the end of the 1967-1973 military dictatorship, also known as the *Colonels' Coup*. In 1977, in the spirit of times that called for freedom of speech and expression, a handful of alternative medical physicians formed the Ellenic Chiropractic, Naturopathic and Osteopathic Physicians' Association (ECNOPA). The Association was composed of the separate associations of the three distinct professions, but for legal purposes had to present itself as

Figure 56. Ancient marble depiction of Asclepius possibly performing a cervical spine manipulation manoeuvre

one association with one constitution, since the formation of a legal union in Greece required a minimum of 20 members. The first President was Socrates Christodoularis DC, DO, ND, CAc (1977-1990). The chiropractic branch of ECNOPA, the Ellenic Chiropractors' Association (ECA), was one of the associations that voted in favour of the formation of the World Federation of Chiropractic (WFC) in London in 1987. Following that, it became a founding member of the WFC during the International Chiropractic Congress in Sydney, Australia in October 1988. Shortly afterwards, in December 1988 the ECA became a member of the ECU.

During the years 1988 and 1989 court cases of major importance for chiropractic took place in Greece. The first case, in 1988, followed applications by Dr Socrates Christodoularis and Dr Eleni Skarpathaki-Karamani for licences to practise chiropractic. The Ministry of Health denied them licences and prohibited them from practising. The matter was taken to the High Court of Appeals, which overturned the Ministry's prohibition, stating that the chiropractic profession was non-medical, non-invasive, and since its practice was not prohibited by any Greek law, then it was permitted. Nevertheless, it was added that Greek law restricted the privilege of delivering diagnoses and treatment of any kind solely to medical doctors. If chiropractic management of patients is not to involve diagnosis and treatment, one might reasonably ask what it

Figure 57. The first chiropractor to practise in Greece, Kleanthis Ligeros
Left: Kleanthis Ligeros MD, PhD, DC. Right: Dr Ligeros' book: Chiropractic, the New Therapeutic Science (1929).

does involve. It is possible to argue, as some of the early chiropractors in the United States did, that the role of chiropractic care is to identify and remove subluxations, nothing more, nothing less, thus allowing the body's natural healing mechanisms to act effectively, rather than focusing on diagnosis or treatment of specific disease conditions. At the same time that this first court case was taking place, so was a second. The Medical Association of Athens indicted Dr Socrates Christodoularis, Dr Eleni Skarpathaki-Karamani, and Dr Eustratios Manolides to Athens District Court under the accusation of practising medicine

without a license. Following an emotional and fierce legal battle, the chiropractors were exonerated. Feeling optimistic from the positive verdict, the following year (1989) Dr Skarpathaki-Karamani appealed to the High Court of Appeals once more, in an effort to allow chiropractors freedom of practice. Although the verdict was again positive for chiropractic, it still disassociated its practice from the diagnosis and treatment of diseases.

In 1990 the ECNOPA was renamed the Ellenic Association for Alternative Medicine (EAsAM). In the years that followed, 1993-

1994, there was internal dispute. Some, but not all of the chiropractors who were members of the EAsAM, abandoned it in order to form an association that was composed exclusively of chiropractors, the Greek Chiropractic Society (GCS). Following careful mediation by the WFC and the ECU, chiropractors in Greece solved their differences, joined forces and formed a new association. They kept the name Ellenic Chiropractors' Association and set a new constitution. The Association as we know it today made its official debut on 11th November 1994. It was independent from the umbrella association, the EAsAM, and its first President was Dr Neoklis Yassemides DC, DO, ND, who served between 1995 and 1996.

The arrival of new chiropractic graduates during the 1990s resulted in an increase in the membership of the ECA and in 2000 a successful ECU convention was held in Athens. The Convention was organised by the then President, Vassilios Maltezopoulos MD, DC, who from then on became the official academic organiser for the ECU, a position which he holds to this day.

Since 2000, the ECA has become increasingly aware of the importance of serious legal representation, as well as the importance of effective political lobbying. Powered by the fresh ideas and energy of the new generation of chiropractors arriving, together with the experience and wisdom of the older generation, a new effort towards chiropractic legislation in Greece started in 2003. The then President of the ECA, Katerina Moustaka MD, DC, formed Greece's first ever patients' association (Pro-Chiropractic Association) in order to raise awareness and gather support to the ECA's cause. In the same spirit, she suggested to the General Assembly of the ECA that they hire the services of a well respected legal advisor who was thought to have the stature and the necessary contacts to achieve a breakthrough where past legal attempts had failed. Since the fees of such an endeavour could not be met by such a small association, in 2004 the ECA applied for financial support from the ECU.

The current President, Vasileios Gkolfinopoulos secured the ECU's financial support at the ECU's General Council meeting in Athens in November 2004. A comprehensive file which supported the need for legislation of the chiropractic profession in Greece was put together and following consecutive meetings with the Deputy Minister and the Minister of Health, the ECA is at this point in time (October 2006) awaiting a hearing with the National Health Council. The struggle for chiropractic legislation continues in Greece, but in the name of public safety and professional justice, the ECA, which today has 25 members, is determined to continue until a satisfactory resolution is achieved.

9. CHIROPRACTIC IN ICELAND

A short history of chiropractic in Iceland, by Tryggvi Jónasson

KEY FACTS: ICELAND
Population: <1 million
National Chiropractic Association: Kírópraktorafélag Íslands
Number of chiropractors registered with National Association (October 2006): 5
President of National Association (October 2006): Katrin Sveinsdóttir

At the beginning of the 1970s 4 Icelanders set out to start an education in chiropractic. Three went to Palmer College of Chiropractic in the United States, Páll Haraldsson, Guðmundur Gudmundsson, and his brother Ludvig Gudmundsson. One, Tryggvi Jónasson (Bjarnason), went to the Anglo-European College of Chiropractic (AECC) in England. Each successfully completed their chiropractic training, graduating between 1975-6. Only one of them, Tryggvi Jónasson, returned to practise in Iceland.

After graduating as a chiropractor, Jónasson went for a period of mandatory postgraduate training in Denmark, where he worked in Aarhus with chiropractors Aase and Henning Hviid. After receiving Danish authorisation to practise, he travelled back to Iceland in 1977. There he started the first chiropractic clinic in Reykjavik. At the time there were few options for people seeking treatment for musculoskeletal conditions in Iceland. There were only a few masseurs, medical doctors and physiotherapists. Within a month of setting up his chiropractic practice Jónasson was approached by the Surgeon General of Iceland and asked to stop practising, as chiropractic was not a licensed profession in Iceland, and was therefore deemed to be quackery, prohibited by law. After he lobbied ministers, especially the Minister of Health, Jónasson was told that if he stopped practising an amendment might be made to Icelandic medical laws that would allow him to make chiropractic an officially licensed practice in Iceland. Jónasson became the first chiropractor practising in Scandinavia to receive an official licence as a chiropractor.

Practising alone in Reykjavik, Jónasson was described as "the loneliest chiropractor in the world", however after some promotional work in the schools of Reykjavik a number of other Icelanders decided to pursue a career in chiropractic. Five Icelanders graduated from the AECC in the years between 1988 and 1992. However, only 3 of these returned to Iceland and only two have remained practising there. In 1989 Katrin Sveinsdóttir started a clinic in Reykjavik and was joined a year later by Gunnar Arnarson. Jónasson, Sveinsdóttir and Arnarson were the founder members of the Icelandic Chiropractors' Association (ICA), which since the early 1990s has been active in its communication and co-operation

Figure 58. Tryggvi Jónasson, Katrin Sveinsdóttir and Gunnar Arnarson: the first chiropractors to practise in Iceland

with other Scandinavian chiropractic associations. The first Nordic Board meeting in Iceland was held in 1992. Present were Gunnar Runberg (Sweden), Per Ingvar Kopp (Sweden), Kyrre Myhrvold (Norway), Lisbeth Lauttho (Finland), Troels Gaarde (Denmark), Gunnar Arnarson, Katrin Sveinsdóttir and Tryggvi Jónasson (Iceland). The ICA participated in the founding development of the Nordic Institute of Chiropractic and Clinical Biomechanics in Odense, Denmark, and to this day there is an Icelandic member on the Board of Governors at the Institute.

In 1994 the chiropractor Solveig Asgeirsdóttir

came to Iceland, and then in 1996, the first American graduate arrived, Bergur Konráðsson, a graduate from Palmer College. Two years later Egill Þorsteinsson, a graduate from Sherman College of Chiropractic, joined the growing number of chiropractors practising in Iceland.

Promotional work during the 1990s resulted in agreements for the reimbursement of chiropractic fees by a number of workers unions. In 2000, the Federation of State and Municipal Employees decided to reimburse chiropractic fees for their members.

The environment in which chiropractors

Figure 59. Officials photographed at the time of Iceland's entry into the ECU in 2001

currently work in Iceland is very different from the environment in which Tryggvi Jónasson found himself in 1977. Today, the Minister of Health grants licenses to those suitably qualified chiropractors who wish to practise in Iceland and the country has its own active chiropractic association. Since 2001 the ICA has been a member of the ECU.

Icelandic chiropractors are currently in discussions with the Ministry of Health and Social Services with the aim of making changes to existing regulations which do not permit chiropractors to own x-ray equipment, or refer patients for x-rays, magnetic resonance imaging, or computerised tomography.

10. CHIROPRACTIC IN IRELAND

A short history of chiropractic in Ireland, by Andrew Doody

KEY FACTS: IRELAND
Population: 4 million
National Chiropractic Association: Chiropractic Association of Ireland
Number of chiropractors registered with National Association (October 2006): 141
President of National Association (October 2006): Jimmy Cosgrave

The origins of chiropractic in Ireland are not clear. Much of the history reported here has had to be retrieved from memory, rather than from records, so word of mouth has been one of the main resources.

From the 1920s onwards the first chiropractors arrived on Irish shores from the United States: Drs Atkins, Bannister, Barret, Buttomer, and Counihan were amongst them. It is thought that in the years prior to the 1960s as many as 40 chiropractors might have practised in Ireland at one time or another, but numbers dwindled to a mere 2 or 3 by the 1960s. Ireland at this time was socio-economically under-developed and conditions would not have been favourable.

The first available written evidence of a chiropractor practising in Ireland is from Dr CER Bannister, who began practising in Ireland in or about 1920. In an issue of the *Chiropractic and Clinical Journal*, published in October 1920, Bannister described the chiropractic aspect in Ireland. Both he and his wife were Palmer graduates and arrived on the shores of Ireland as pioneers of chiropractic. Articles by him during this period describe an island of political unrest, but one which yearned for more chiropractic leaders to advance the profession. Bannister went on to become the first President of the ECU in 1932, a position which he held for many years. He was also responsible for forming what was probably the first association of chiropractors in Europe, the short-lived Chiropractors' Association of the British Isles, established in 1922. His daughter Muriel, also a chiropractor, was married to a Dr W Brownrigg who served as Secretary to the British Chiropractors' Association (BCA) for many years.

Drs Deasy, MagCuill and Brown established chiropractic practices in the South of Ireland during the 1960s, despite what would appear to have been considerable resistance from mainstream medicine. Dr Deasy was a Palmer graduate of 1963, who after graduating worked initially in London as a member of the BCA. Later, he returned to Ireland and settled in Bantry, where he began practising due to public demand after he treated a neighbour. Word quickly got around regarding the success of his treatment. He passed away in Bantry in 1994. Dr MagCuill who was a graduate of Logan College of Chiropractic, practised first in Nova Scotia, Canada, before coming to Dublin in 1963, where he stayed and worked successfully until 1983, when he was struck down with myalgic encephalomyelitis (ME) and forced to retire.

In the late 1970s there were probably about half a dozen chiropractors working in Ireland, most of whom were Sherman College graduates, who favoured *straight* chiropractic philosophy (adjusting the spine only). It was this group that were responsible for forming the first Irish association of chiropractors, and in 1985 Dr B Tague became the first President of the Chiropractic Association of Ireland (CAI). Its aim was to unite and provide support for chiropractors working in Ireland. Shortly afterwards, in 1988, the CAI was accepted into the ECU and new graduates wishing to be members were required to have

Figure 60. Charles ER Bannister (centre) with colleagues at an ECU meeting in 1939. Notice the posters on the wall, which were produced in support of the attempt to achieve statutory recognition for chiropractic in Zürich, Switzerland at the time.

Figure 61. From left to right, Drs Finley, Tague, Dawson and Dawson, circa 1985

qualifications recognised by the Council on Chiropractic Education / European Council on Chiropractic Education. In 1997 there were 44 members of the CAI. Since then the number of chiropractors practising in Ireland has increased significantly and there are now over 150 chiropractors working on these shores.

At present, the chiropractic profession is not regulated by statute in Ireland and this creates problems for the public, for the government, and for chiropractors alike, although chiropractors do practise with a freedom that is not found in some other European countries. Much of the work currently being done by the CAI is in creating an environment where the factors necessary for statutory regulation are met. This is our biggest challenge at the moment.

11. CHIROPRACTIC IN ITALY

A short history of chiropractic in Italy, by Thomas E Rigel

KEY FACTS: ITALY
Population: 59 million
National Chiropractic Association: Associazione Italiana Chiropratici
Number of chiropractors registered with National Association (October 2006): 180
President of National Association (October 2006): John Williams
Website: www.associazionechiropratici.it

As is frequently the case with history, dates and facts are often times missing, and the story of chiropractic in Italy is no exception. Although there is documentary evidence that suggests that chiropractic activity existed in Italy some 60 years ago, there is reason to believe that chiropractic was introduced much earlier. The name of a certain Dr Pistolesi lingers in the minds of a few, who believe that this person was indeed a chiropractor who practised in Rome as early as 1920.

Documentary evidence supports the fact that Dr Marcello Trentin established a full-time practice in Italy in the late 1940s. Born in the north-eastern part of Italy, Marcello as a boy and young man proved to be inquisitive, bright, and determined. In fact, even though disadvantaged by World War I injuries, he persevered to obtain his Doctor of Chiropractic from National College of Chiropractic in 1928. As was common to the time, Dr Trentin was absorbed into the great melting pot of multi-national immigration into the United States of America. It was not until 1949, that he left his successful Palm Beach, Florida practice to return to Italy. There his professional career and fame grew in the city of Padova, where his clinical proficiency and impeccable professional behaviour gained the admiration of even would be critics. Dr Trentin's accomplishments inspired an entrepreneur to bring chiropractic into a medical practice in Milan, and a medical doctor to send two of his offspring to a chiropractic college in America.

Amongst the names of the first chiropractors to practise in Italy are Hans Greissing, and Giacomo and Caterina Palatini. By 1969 2 French chiropractors, Dr Gilbert Meyronet and Dr Marc Perier, had established a part-time practice in Genova, and chiropractic services could also be found in Rome. By the early 1970s the Italian chiropractic profession was a multi-national collection of individuals, which although numbering less than 20 in all, included French, American, Belgian, Canadian, Swiss, English, and three Italian chiropractors. In 1974 the Italian Chiropractors' Association, the *Associazione Italiana Chiropratici* (AIC), was founded and entered the ECU.

Chiropractic in Italy experienced a growth

Figure 62. Photographs of Marcello Trentin's chiropractic office as it was in the late 1960s

surge during the following decade, as many chiropractors found employment in specially designed medical clinics. An organisation called Static led the way in integrating chiropractic services into medical practices. The integration of chiropractic principles and techniques into a medical framework proved to be legally acceptable and opened the gate to state healthcare contracts, rendering chiropractic services free to all Italians. Within a short period of time Static established clinics in the major cities of Italy. With skilful and successful management, it became a whirlwind of activity. The enterprise soon counted more than 500 active personnel, receiving more than 1,000 new patients a week, and delivering over 1,000,000 treatments per year, becoming one of the largest operations delivering chiropractic services that the profession has ever known. Many foreign chiropractors were rotated through Italy under this system, and hundreds of thousands of Italians were exposed

to this particular version of chiropractic care. Parallel to this phenomenon was the gradual growth of traditional individual chiropractic practices, both with and without medical collaboration. These practices represented only a minority of the overall profession and had little influence on the political evolution of chiropractic at the time, which was largely controlled by entrepreneurs from outside the profession.

In 1980 a commission was formed within the Health Ministry to examine chiropractic. The inquest, supported by positive statistical data and first hand investigation, concluded that chiropractic was useful and effective. Their report recommended that chiropractic should be accepted as a legitimate healthcare occupation, and that educational facilities and legislation should be provided. In order to implement its usage, and the potential for increasing demand for chiropractic services,

Figure 63. A lesson in posture. An illustration from a booklet, produced partly in English and partly in Italian, by Marcello Trentin entitled: La Chiropratica - Fonte della Salute Naturale - The Physician-Radio-Engineer of the Future – Today.

guidelines were established for a medical framework in which chiropractors could work. Treatment parameters and the minimal requisites for foreign workers' permits were also specified.

Of substantial importance to the emerging profession were the administrative / bureaucratic skirmishes and court conflicts in which chiropractors found themselves protagonists. At their core, the disputes centred on non-recognition of chiropractic degrees and the accusation of practising medicine without a license. One of these cases went so far as to the Constitutional Court for decision. The court noted, as had the lower courts previously, that the chiropractors maintained that they were practising chiropractic, not medicine, and that nothing in Italian law either defined chiropractic or prohibited its use. Therefore the

defendants had a constitutional right to work and sustain themselves by using chiropractic as a vocational art. This seemingly positive verdict, which basically sustained *straight chiropractic* as a non-diagnostic and non-therapeutic practice, opened a floodgate to *pseudo-practitioners*. Nothing prohibited the use of the title *Doctor of Chiropractic*. Hundreds proclaimed to be chiropractors, courses were invented and the diploma mills set their gears in action. To further confuse the public, there were clinical boundary disputes with physiotherapists, osteopaths, medical manipulators and dentists. In time, the media related stories of people being harmed and even crippled by so-called chiropractors.

Over the decades, growing awareness of chiropractic in Italy has been facilitated by a significant amount of media attention. The

Static group advanced the merits of what they called *chiroterapia*. The profession also fell into limelight when chiropractors obtained media attention by associating themselves with celebrities and other renowned figures. The image of chiropractic was further enhanced by notations of chiropractic success stories, especially in the field of sports. Currently, even though there is still a fair amount of journalistic attention given to chiropractic, its image has been somewhat tarnished as a result of unprotected practice, the lack of protection of title.

Following a national survey in which it was found that 9 million Italians were utilizing alternative medicines, the National Federation for the Orders of Medical Doctors and Dentists determined in May 2002 that chiropractic and 8 alternative medical practices were to be considered as "acts of medicine" and therefore be practised only by members of their Federation. Subsequent to this position being taken by the Medical Federation, legal ramifications rapidly unfolded. The Italian Supreme Court followed the Federation's lead and overturned lower court sentences that had acquitted chiropractors from the accusation of practising medicine without a license. The Supreme Court stated that everything that a chiropractor has been prepared to do and does, according to existing Italian law, is to be considered an act of medicine. The verdict provoked a wave of federal police investigations, arrest warrants and court trials. The consequences of the Court's decision are still being seen.

Shortly after the position paper published by the National Federation for the Orders of Medical Doctors and Dentists, a proposal for a law to regulate non-conventional medical practices was pushed to the forefront of parliamentary affairs. AIC proposals for law dating back to 1991 were dissected and formed a foundation for a unified text for proposed regulation of alternative medical practices. Under possible legislation, chiropractors might be given rights as non-medical healthcare providers. Time will tell.

Not withstanding the havoc described above, it seems certain that given the commitment, perseverance and stamina that the chiropractic profession has always demonstrated through its history, chiropractors in Italy will find ways and means to apply their "Art, Science and Philosophy" for the benefit of patients.

12. CHIROPRACTIC IN LIECHTENSTEIN

A short history of chiropractic in Liechtenstein, by Beatrice Mikus and Christopher Mikus

---

KEY FACTS: LIECHTENSTEIN
Population: <1 million
National Chiropractic Association: Verein Liechtensteiner Chiropraktoren
Number of chiropractors registered with National Association (October 2006): 4
President of National Association (October 2006): Claudia B. Mikus-Kluchnik

---

The first chiropractic practice in the Principality of Liechtenstein was opened in June of 1984 by Beatrice Mikus, DC. This chiropractic pioneer is a graduate of the Los Angeles College of Chiropractic and a native of Liechtenstein. At that time, chiropractic was virtually unknown in the country and consequently, acquiring a niche in the political healthcare field proved to be a significant challenge. In Liechtenstein during the early and mid 1980s there already existed a law pertaining to chiropractic, this being due to the fact that the law in Liechtenstein that governed the educational and scope of practice issues of healthcare professions (*Sanitaetsgesetz*) was almost identical to that of Liechtenstein's neighbour, Switzerland. Gaining recognition, though, such that the local insurance companies would pay for chiropractic services, proved to be a greater challenge. However, after much effort on the part of Dr Mikus, this was also attained in 1985.

Several years later, Dr Mikus had the pleasure of including her daughter, Claudia Mikus-Kluchnik, DC, and son, Christopher Mikus, DC, into the Liechtenstein chiropractic family. Over the ensuing years, this chiropractic family was able to build acceptance for the profession, as evidenced by a large patient following, as well as growing respect among government officials and other healthcare professionals. In 1995 these 3 chiropractors founded the first chiropractic association in Liechtenstein, *Verband Liechtensteiner Chiropraktoren*. In November 1998 this Association was accepted as a full member into the European Chiropractors' Union. The Liechtenstein Chiropractic Association currently consists of 4 members, its 4th member being Markus Kindle.

As in most other countries within Europe, the skyrocketing costs of healthcare have become an ever-growing concern in Liechtenstein. Since the late 1990s all Liechtenstein healthcare providers have been requested to help reduce their costs. Such a situation tends to lead to competition between professions. In 2001 an attempt was made by local politicians, at the behest of a powerful medical lobby, to limit the number of treatments a chiropractic patient could receive without a referral from his or her medical doctor to 6 visits. This action would have rendered chiropractors as mere therapists, despite their thorough

Figure 64. The founding members of the Liechtenstein Chiropractic Association. From left to right: Claudia Mikus-Kluchnik, Beatrice Mikus, and Christopher Mikus.

education and training in neuromusculoskeletal diagnosis. Of course, this action resulted in resistance from both chiropractors and their patients. Following a political push on the part of Liechtenstein's chiropractic association and by a few politically well-positioned patients, the need for medical referral was removed.

Chiropractic has now become an integral part of the healthcare system in Liechtenstein. Chiropractic services are included in the obligatory portion of the sickness and healthcare insurance, *Krankenversicherungsgesetz*. This means that every resident of the country is entitled to consult his or her chiropractor as needed, with the costs covered by their health insurance. In addition, the referral of patients by chiropractors for x-rays, computerised tomography, magnetic resonance imaging, and for physical therapy has also been recognised. Another significant milestone for the profession was achieved in 2004. Chiropractors achieved the same legal status as other accepted healthcare professionals, such as medical doctors, dentists, and pharmacists. Presently, there are 3 chiropractors practising in the tiny Principality, while the pioneer of chiropractic in Liechtenstein enjoys a well-deserved retirement!

13. CHIROPRACTIC IN LUXEMBOURG

A short history of chiropractic in Luxembourg, by Louis Stephany

KEY FACTS: LUXEMBOURG
Population: <1 million
National Chiropractic Association: Chiroletzebuerg
Number of chiropractors registered with National Association (October 2006): 5
President of National Association (October 2006): Louis Stephany

The Grand Duchy of Luxembourg is one of the smallest countries in Europe, with a population of under half a million people, yet it is a country that boasts a full and colourful history, a nation that today is economically and politically integrated with other parts of Europe. It was a founder member of the European Union and of the United Nations. The European Court of Justice and the Secretariat of the European Parliament (the administrative body of the European Parliament) are both based in Luxembourg.

In the early part of the twentieth century a variety of natural healing methods were popular in the neighbouring country of Germany, so much so that by the 1930s there were roughly as many lay practitioners as qualified medical doctors practising there. In 1939 the Nazi Government created the *Heilpraktiker* to officially recognise lay practitioners, but also to control them and restrict their growth. As in Germany, homeopathic and other natural healing methods were popular in Luxembourg at the time, and there were fears within medical ranks that the country would see increasing numbers of these practitioners. In response,

medical doctors lobbied for greater protection of what they perceived to be their field. An environment that was unsympathetic to non-conventional medicines developed, one in which the Luxembourgish Medical College opposed the advancement of complementary and alternative medicine.

Over the years there were a number of cases where practitioners of non-conventional therapies were prosecuted in Luxembourg. In 1980 for example, the guru of a large healing sect was condemned by the Luxembourgish Court of Justice for illegal exercise of medicine. In 1984, a chiropractor working in Belgium made a complaint about a medical doctor associated with the same sect. Thanks to the collaboration of the chiropractor, the Medical College and Luxembourgish authorities were able to take severe disciplinary action against the medical doctor concerned, such as had not been seen before in the history of Luxembourg. The case attracted significant media attention within Luxembourg and also internationally, and increased hostility towards non-conventional healthcare practices within the Grand Duchy.

Under Luxembourgish Law, the treatment,

diagnosis and prevention of disease has been restricted to those with an accepted medical qualification. There has been no law governing chiropractic and in the absence of an environment conducive to chiropractic practice, patients have travelled to neighbouring countries to receive chiropractic care. This has been the case until very recently, however, in the last few years there has been an increasing air of tolerance towards chiropractic and other non-conventional healthcare disciplines in Luxembourg. As recently as 2000 chiropractic was portrayed in a negative light in a proposal for law, however the period since 2000 has seen some very positive developments

for chiropractic. In January 2003, Louis Stephany, a chiropractor practising in Belgium, was asked by Depute Jean Colombera, a medical doctor, to present evidence on chiropractic to a commission of enquiry into non-conventional medicines. With the aid of the Anglo-European College of Chiropractic (AECC), information was gathered which emphasised the high academic standards of chiropractic education internationally. An invitation was issued by Dr Kenneth Vall of the AECC to those involved in the commission to visit the College in order to gain a better understanding of chiropractic. In October 2003, chiropractic received positive media

Figure 65. Depute Jean Colombera (right), a medical doctor supportive of chiropractic, with chiropractor Louis Stephany (left), following debate in the Luxembourgish Chamber of Deputies, 2004

attention when a programme on national television described a patient travelling from Luxembourg for chiropractic treatment in Belgium. In January 2004 the commission on non-conventional / complementary medicine reported its findings to Luxembourg's Chamber of Deputies, the body vested with legislative power for the Grand Duchy. There was a call for chiropractic to be recognised as an official health profession (and also for osteopathy to be recognised), and a motion was put forward to change legislation that gives only medical doctors the right to diagnose. At the end of the session a vote was taken on the motion. It was passed with 51 votes for and 2 against. Although this has not yet resulted in a change in law, it has marked the first official acceptance of chiropractic in Luxembourg and has brought about a new tolerance towards chiropractic from the Ministry of Health.

It appears that a new more tolerant era for healthcare in Luxembourg might be beginning. Chiropractors are now coming to Luxembourg to set up in practice. Probably the first was Alexandre Fremeaux, a graduate of the Institut Franco-Européen de Chiropratique, Paris, who first saw patients in Luxembourg in 2002. Another chiropractor, Scott Oliver, a Canadian graduate of Sherman College of Straight Chiropractic in the United States, started a practice in Luxembourg in January 2005. Recently, Bruno Classens has joined Fremeaux's practice. The current President of Chiroletzebuerg, the chiropractic association of Luxembourg which was formed in April 2004, is Louis Stephany. He currently practises in the village of Thiaumont, Belgium, but also has an office in the Grand Duchy to which he is planning to transfer his practice. There are currently five members of Chiroletzebuerg: Bruno Claessens, Marie-Christine Cousin-Armand (practising in Belgium), Alexandre Fremeaux, Scott Oliver and Louis Stephany.

Chiroletzebuerg became a member of the ECU in 2005, the most recent addition to the Union. Chiroletzebuerg and the ECU President Philippe Druart have been working to promote chiropractic in Luxembourg and it is hoped that in the near future there will be statutory regulation of chiropractic in the Grand Duchy.

14. CHIROPRACTIC IN THE NETHERLANDS

A short history of chiropractic in the Netherlands, by Ben Bolsenbroek

KEY FACTS: THE NETHERLANDS
Population: 16 million
National Chiropractic Association: Nederlandse Chiropractoren Associatie
Number of chiropractors registered with National Association (October 2006): 193
President of National Association (October 2006): Jan Gert Wagenaar

It was thought by some that the first chiropractor to practise in the Netherlands did so from 1968, however, it has recently come to light that there were chiropractors practising there many years before this. With the help of family members, these people's names and stories have now been added to the history of chiropractic in the Netherlands.

Two brothers, John and Pieter van der Meer, graduated from the Palmer School of Chiropractic, in Davenport, Iowa, in 1923. John worked as a chiropractor in The Hague for 3 years, but fell foul of a judicial system that did not recognise chiropractic. He gave up his chiropractic practice and went to work in his father's bakery. He never practised chiropractic again. Due to the legal difficulties associated with practising chiropractic in the Netherlands, Pieter van der Meer chose not to work as a chiropractor in the Netherlands at all. He opened a furniture shop instead. Another chiropractor, Jan Hendrik Schoemakers, opened an office in Rotterdam in 1926. He practised there for 10 years, but he also came under pressure to stop his chiropractic work, labelled as a quack. In the end he decided to leave the Netherlands and return to the United States where he had qualified. So it was that the first chiropractors to practise chiropractic in the Netherlands found the environment so unaccommodating that the profession was unable to establish itself successfully. It would be more than 40 years before another chiropractor would attempt to set up practice in the country.

The intervening years did see the successful professional development of at least one chiropractor of Dutch decent, Joseph Janse. Janse was born on the Island of Walcheren, the Netherlands, in 1909. He studied at National College of Chiropractic in Chicago in the years between 1935 and 1938. Upon graduation he did not return to his homeland, but chose instead to pursue his career in the United States. There, in time, he became one of the most respected figures in the history of chiropractic, an educator and researcher, known for his work in the fields of anatomy and biomechanics, the third President of the National College of Chiropractic, a position which he held for 38 years. It was in significant part due to the efforts of Janse that the *Journal of Manipulative and Physiological Therapeutics* (JMPT), a journal which continues to be

Figure 66. Dutch chiropractic students Ype Brandsma and Tjeerd Kramer (wearing clinic jackets, front row left and right respectively) with fellow students at the Anglo-European College of Chiropractic in the 1980s

produced to this day, came to be.

The modern history of chiropractic in the Netherlands begins in the 1960s when engineer Frits Speijers, having experienced chiropractic in the United States, could find no chiropractor to continue his care upon return to the Netherlands. Forced to go to Belgium for treatment, Frits and his friend JJ Merz founded an association, *Nederlandse Vereniging Pro Chiropractie* (NVPC) in 1965, to encourage chiropractors to come to the Netherlands. Their call was answered. In 1968 DP de Koekkoek opened a clinic in Utrecht. One year later he was followed by his brother G de Koekkoek, who came to practise in Amsterdam, and later

D van Os in Vinkeveen. Like their predecessors, each of these practitioners was put under pressure to stop practising chiropractic. Unlike their predecessors, these chiropractors successfully resisted attempts to stop them practising their art.

Also in the 1960s, there were a group of Dutch physiotherapists who began to use chiropractic techniques. It is said that Frits Philips, the Director of the Philips Company, on one of his oversees travels to New Zealand during the 1950s, suffered from low back pain. His host took him to his family chiropractor, Dr Phelps. The story goes that Philips made a remarkable recovery following his chiropractic treatment and then decided to have Phleps introduce his physiotherapists to chiropractic. In 1967 this led to the start of an educational institute of manual therapy in Eindhoven, now known as the *Methode Eindhoven*.

The first female chiropractor to practise in the Netherlands, and the first to have graduated from the Anglo-European College of Chiropractic, was Liesbeth Vis, who started her chiropractic practice in Rotterdam in 1973. Soon after her arrival in the Netherlands movements were made towards the formation of an association of chiropractors there. The Netherlands Chiropractors' Association (NCA), *Nederlandse Vereniging van Chiropractoren*, became an official entity on 9th July 1975. Its laws and bye-laws were set up with the aid of Meip en Christ van Beest, an ex-President of the South-African Chiropractors' Association.

In the years since its formation, the NCA has grown and matured. In 2005 it celebrated its 30th anniversary. Today members of the NCA are also registered with the *Stichting Chiropractie Nederland* (SCN), a quality control foundation which only accepts those who meet high standards in chiropractic, educationally and professionally, and participate in continuing professional development. This organisation has had a positive impact on the Association and has also had a positive impact on the view of chiropractic from the perspective of insurers.

There are now nearly 200 members of the

NCA, with further growth expected, but members of the Association have not always been able to meet the demand from the public for chiropractic in the Netherlands. In 1992 a national prime-time television programme on chiropractic caused a flood of interest from the public, many of whom called their local chiropractor. Chiropractors have never again encouraged such a programme to be aired, as the enormity of interest in 1992 was too huge for the chiropractors to cope with effectively. The NCA alone received 35,000 letters with requests for information!

In 1986 a bill was passed unanimously in the

Figure 67. Jan Gert Wagenaar, President of the Netherlands Chiropractors' Association, at celebrations to mark the Association's 30th anniversary

second chamber of the Dutch Parliament to recognise and regulate chiropractic. Unfortunately, 20 years later, this has not been activated, and chiropractic remains without effective regulatory control under law. The NCA continues to work towards the statutory regulation of chiropractic in the Netherlands and in this has received support from the World Health Organisation (WHO), the World Federation of Chiropractic (WFC) and the European Chiropractors' Union (ECU). The Association remains optimistic, despite the fact that in recent years chiropractors have not been allowed to take x-rays, even though they study both radiography and radiology in their undergraduate studies.

At the present time efforts are being made to establish a school of chiropractic in the Netherlands, linked to the university system. A working group with financial support from the ECU and also from a physiotherapy fund have produced a strategic document. Initial contacts with universities have been made. The publication of WHO guidelines on basic training and safety in chiropractic in 2006 could not have come at a better time. We feel confident that these guidelines will help our cause.

15. CHIROPRACTIC IN NORWAY

A short history of chiropractic in Norway, by Øystein Ogre

KEY FACTS: NORWAY
Population: 5 million
National Chiropractic Association: Norsk Kiropraktorforening
Number of chiropractors registered with National Association (October 2006): 364
President of National Association (October 2006): Øystein Ogre
Website: www.kiropraktikk.no

Arthur E Lundh was the first chiropractor who is known to have established a practice in Norway, in the year 1922. There are, however, records from Palmer School of Chiropractic which name two other Norwegians, Marie S Nesseth and C Rasmussen, who studied chiropractic there in 1906.

Arthur Lundh had served in the United States Army during World War I, working as a nurse in a field hospital in France. After the War he was discharged from the army at Camp Dodge, Iowa, a short distance from Palmer School of Chiropractic in Davenport. There he chose to study chiropractic, and as a war veteran, the United States government agreed to pay his educational fees. He graduated as a chiropractor in 1921. Initially he set up practice in Wheaton, Illinois, but it was not long before he decided to return to Norway, to Kristiania, now Oslo, in November 1922. Arthur Lundh practised chiropractic alone in Norway until a chance meeting in a hotel in 1924, where he was having lunch. He was seated next to a couple of Americans and having introduced himself found that the visitors were Joe Ohman, a Norwegian who was living in America, who happened to be a chiropractor, and his wife Daisy. Within a couple of hours, Arthur Lundh managed to persuade them to cancel their reservation for that afternoon's sailing to the United States and settle in Norway!

Over the following years other chiropractors joined them and by 1935 there were 20 or so chiropractors in Norway. These were times when the Norwegian Medical Association took an aggressive stance towards chiropractic. There were negative articles in major newspapers, where chiropractic was called quackery and humbug. Arthur Lundh had found himself in court in 1932 for violating the "Quack" law, and was accused of treating a patient with a horseshoe-shaped instrument (this was in fact a neurocalometer, a device used to help in the identification of spinal lesions). Lundh was acquitted, in large part due to the testimony of some medical doctors that he called as witnesses.

The situation became quite uncomfortable for chiropractors in Norway and they felt the need to become organised. Arthur Lundh took the lead. The Norwegian Chiropractors' Association (NCA) was founded on the 29th August 1935. Following its formation Lundh was for many years the natural leader of the Association. During his years in practice he wrote many articles defending chiropractic in

Figure 68. Kyrre Myhrvold, President of the Norwegian Chiropractors' Association from 1986 to 1994

the newspapers and wrote 3 books about chiropractic. Arthur E Lundh was the President of the NCA until about 1950. He died in 1977 at the age of 87.

Another force for chiropractic's advancement in Norway was Kyrre Myhrvold. From the time of his graduation as a chiropractor to the time of his death in 2003 at the age of 57, Kyrre Myhrvold was involved in political work for the Norwegian Chiropractors' Association. He served as its President from 1986 until 1994, and was involved in all the major chiropractic reforms and achievements in Norway through those years. Myrhvold was also a chiropractic historian. In the late 1990s he began working in conjunction with the ECU to draw together histories of chiropractic from the nations of Europe. His work led to the book that you are now reading.

Table 11. *Presidents of the Norwegian Chiropractors'*
Association, 1935-2006

Arthur E. Lundh	1935 – circa 1950
Alv Heum	circa 1950 – 1960
Olav Kaugerud	1960 – 1980
Trond Soot	1980 – 1986
Kyrre Myhrvold	1986 – 1994
Espen Johannessen	1994 – 1998
Eli Magnesen	1998 – 2002
Øystein Ogre	2002 –

The first attempt that chiropractors made to gain legislation for chiropractic in Norway came in 1936. It was ignored by the authorities. The next attempt came in 1953. At that time a public committee concluded that chiropractic was unscientific. In 1974, however, the Norwegian Parliament voted in favour of reimbursement of chiropractic treatment fees in cases where the patient had been referred to the chiropractor by a medical doctor. This arrangement was meant to be temporary, but remained in effect until 1st January 2006. Legislation to regulate chiropractic in Norway was finally achieved in 1988. The legislation followed 5 years of work by a governmental committee with chiropractic representation. The following chiropractors were central to this work: Olav Kaugerud, Kyrre Myhrvold, Trond Soot, Georg Rasmussen and Anfinn Kilvaer.

In 1999 the Norwegian Parliament decided to initiate a trial involving chiropractic, to last for a period of 2 years and involve 3 different Norwegian counties. Chiropractors were given the right to authorise sick leave, refer patients to hospital, including to medical specialists and physiotherapists. Patients received direct reimbursement of fees. The trial started in September 2001. The results were evaluated by the independent research organisation known as SINTEF (The Foundation for Scientific and Industrial Research). Results showed that patients had fewer and shorter episodes of sick leave under the new scheme. Patient satisfaction levels were also high. Of fundamental importance was that the arrangement appeared to have positive financial implications. In June 2005 the Norwegian Parliament voted to extend the rights of chiropractors in accordance with the findings of the trial. A new law allowing chiropractors across the whole country extended rights was signed by the King in December 2005 and came into effect from 1st January 2006. This is a significant step for chiropractic in Norway, a step that places chiropractors on a level with medical doctors and epitomises the acceptance of chiropractic within Norwegian society that has come about in recent years.

Throughout the recent development of the profession in Norway the work of the NCA and its members has been crucial. For the past 20 years the NCA has organised a one year postgraduate education programme for those wishing to practise chiropractic in Norway. In 2003 the government made that programme mandatory. Since 2003 it has been making payments to chiropractors working as supervisors on the programme, and since 2004 there has been a government-backed fund to support the continuing professional development of those who practise chiropractic in Norway.

16. CHIROPRACTIC IN PORTUGAL

A short history of chiropractic in Portugal, by Edward M Saltys

---

KEY FACTS: PORTUGAL
Population: 11 million
National Chiropractic Association: Associação Portuguesa dos Quiropráticos
Number of chiropractors registered with National Association (October 2006): 22
President of National Association (October 2006): António Alves

---

In 1984, 10 years after political revolution, Portugal was in the process of socio-political reconstruction, aiming to integrate into the European Union. Until then, the country was governed by successive reforms of a system of dictatorship. Although this was then replaced by a democratic system, ruled by a multi-party assembly, the country continues to use the old bureaucratic public service structures already in place. The health sector is legislated according to Napoleonic code and therefore medicine is legal, while non-legislated practices within the sector are technically illegal. In this system, the national medical association, *Ordem dos Medicos*, has a great deal of influence and has held back attempts to legislate for complementary and alternative medicines (CAM).

There were 4 recorded legal actions against chiropractors between 1993 and 2000. For various reasons, and in all cases, the charges were dropped by the judge at the court hearings. Positive statements were made about chiropractic by a number of judges, such as, "based upon their educational diploma and license to practise, chiropractors have the right to use the title doctor and to be considered specialists of the spine". Another judge stated that "the accused were within their scope of practice to prescribe x-rays based upon their education". No one has ever been fined or gone to jail for practising chiropractic in Portugal.

António F Alves, who is of Portuguese descent, was the first known chiropractor to settle and start a practice in Portugal. Born in the north of the country, but raised in France, he returned to his homeland after graduating with a Doctor of Chiropractic from Life University in Atlanta, Georgia. From the time he arrived in Guarda in early 1986, Dr Alves started to make an impact on the health of the local population and the word of *quiroprática* quickly spread. In that first year he started to work with a lawyer towards the formation of a chiropractors' association. His vision also included plans to create a chiropractic patients' association.

Since the arrival of Dr Alves, a number of North American chiropractors have come to work in Portugal. The first of these is thought to have been Dr Lyle Grenz who settled in Estoril. Several lay people have also taken a

Figure 69. In March 2005 officials from the European Chiropractors' Union and the Portuguese Chiropractic Association met in Portugal to discuss the possibility of a convention to be held in 2007 and jointly organised by the World Federation of Chiropractic, the European Chiropractors' Union, and by the Portuguese Chiropractic Association

keen interest in promoting chiropractic in Portugal. One such person is the lawyer, Dr António Pires da Fonseca, who donated much of his time to the development of chiropractic in Portugal with Dr Alves.

Although the Portuguese people have for generations relied heavily on the medical profession for their healthcare needs, chiropractic has been able to enter their consciousness. The actions of the pioneering chiropractors, and of others who have shared their beliefs and visions, have helped to

advance chiropractic's position. In the presence of deficiencies within the healthcare system, chiropractic's approach to health and wellness has gained significant acceptance amongst the general population. On 1st February 1999, the *Associação Portuguesa dos Quiropráticos* (APQ) was registered in Guarda. January 2000 saw the birth of a chiropractic patients' association, *Pro-Quiro*. The profession is indebted to Dr Alves and Dr Pires da Fonseca for their work, which was instrumental in setting up these associations. Dr Pires da Fonseca continues to act as a lawyer for both associations. Since its formation, Pro-Quiro has helped tremendously with the advancement of chiropractic in Portugal. For his part, Dr Alves has endlessly given of his time and money to develop chiropractic. In 2000 he arranged for a European meeting of the International Chiropractors Association in Lisbon, an event which helped to give the APQ international credibility. Over the years the APQ has attempted to communicate with the Portuguese Minister of Health. Drs Alves and Pires da Fonseca have worked towards statutory regulation of chiropractic in Portugal, specifically to have the titles *chiropractic* and *chiropractor* protected under law.

During the 1990s some schools not accredited by the European Council on Chiropractic Education (ECCE) started to incorporate chiropractic techniques into their natural healthcare courses. There were also chiropractors who harmed the profession by teaching chiropractic techniques to lay people. The APQ's lawyer frequently communicated in writing with those who were deemed to be inappropriately using the titles chiropractic and chiropractor, in an effort to clarify and inform them about the high standards expected by the international chiropractic community. In 2001 a new health bill that would have included coverage of chiropractic was due to be signed in Parliament, but the government resigned that day, delaying legalisation for chiropractic and also for a group of other healthcare professions. With the delay in legislation, the number of those that might be considered

pseudo-chiropractors grew. Compounding the problem has been the fact that some medical practitioners, who have studied manual manipulation in Germany, have professed to practise chiropractic in Portugal.

Chiropractic was finally legalised in Portugal on 22nd August 2003. The bill that was passed in August 2003 did not give chiropractic a category of its own within the health system, and unfortunately it used the Brazilian spelling of chiropractic, *Quiropraxia*. This has caused more work for Dr Alves and Pro-Quiro, who have formally requested to have it changed to

Figure 70. Flyer for the Vilamoura Convention, 2007

Figure 71. The logo of the Portuguese Chiropractic Association

the Portuguese spelling, *Quiroprática*. The Bill specified for a technical commission to implement the regulation of each of the 6 appointed "alternative therapies". The Commission initiated their work in May 2005. Thanks to Pro-Quiro's influence, Dr Alves was selected as the chiropractic representative for the Commission by the Ministry of Health. Up to this point, the profession has presented to the Commission various documents as requested.

Chiropractic would almost certainly be more highly regarded in Portugal if a chiropractic school that met ECCE academic standards was established by the profession to provide education at national level.

Today, chiropractic in Portugal is a legalised profession, with a registered association, and is generally well accepted by the public. The battle for advancement of chiropractic, for its effective regulation and protection, continues to be a major focus for the members of the APQ. The APQ is recognized by its logo, which was designed and first presented in 2005. The curved lines are symbolic of the spine and a hand. As of October 2006 there were 22 registered members, but the number of chiropractors in Portugal continues to grow. For many years chiropractic practices tended to be located in the Lisbon and Algarve areas, but this is changing, and qualified chiropractors can now be found in several other regions of the country.

In May of 2007, 75 years after the formation of the ECU, and 100 years after chiropractic first arrived in Europe, the APQ welcomes chiropractors from across the World to Vilamoura, to celebrate the past, the present and the future of the chiropractic profession. This important convention is jointly organised by the World Federation of Chiropractic, the European Chiropractors' Union, and by the Portuguese Chiropractic Association.

17. CHIROPRACTIC IN SPAIN

A short history of chiropractic in Spain, by Jeff Heese, written in memory of Christopher Hadley and Robert Burciaga, co-founders of the Spanish Chiropractic Association

KEY FACTS: SPAIN
Population: 44 million
National Chiropractic Association: Asociación Española de Quiropráctica
Number of chiropractors registered with National Association (October 2006): 140
President of National Association (October 2006): Belén Sunyer
Website: www.quiropractica-aeq.com

Spain is one of the most ancient and unique countries in Europe. Phoenicians, Greeks, Romans, Visigoths, and Muslims were drawn to Spain's natural resources, strategic geographic position, and temperate climate. This gives the peninsula an historic richness and cultural diversity which continues to heavily influence many areas of modern day Spanish life. One of these areas is healthcare, of which chiropractic is a growing part.

The history of chiropractic in Spain dates back to the second decade of the twentieth century. The first chiropractor to practise in Spain was the Spanish born Pedro Alborna Soler. Upon graduating from the Palmer School of Chiropractic (PSC) in 1917†, he worked in New York for five years before returning to Spain and opening his clinic in Barcelona. He joined other European chiropractors in forming the European Chiropractic Union in 1932. During the Spanish Civil War a few years later, Dr Soler requested, and was sent aid by some of his fellow ECU members. He was a lifelong bachelor, and treated patients until about 1958.

One of Pedro Soler's patients was Amadeo Morera Villadrosa, who as a young man had fallen from a fig tree and seriously injured his spine. He experienced such tremendous results from chiropractic care that he decided to dedicate his life to the profession, and became Spain's second chiropractor when he graduated from PSC in 1959. He opened his clinic in Barcelona that same year. The awareness of chiropractic and its benefits were heightened when Dr Morera began to treat well known individuals, and patients came from great distances to receive an adjustment. He continues to practise, and has no plans to retire.

One of Dr Morera's patients was Jose Luis Cunill Amat. He went on to become Spain's third chiropractor upon graduation from PSC in 1965 and later married Dr Morera's sister. Dr Cunill presently practises with his son Jose Luis Cunill Morera DC, Spain's first second generation chiropractor.

Technically chiropractic has always been neither legal nor illegal in Spain, as no legislation has been passed concerning it, and

Figure 72. Robert Gevers, the first President of the Spanish Chiropractic Association

this has been a problem for chiropractors who have found themselves effectively in a legal limbo. In 1974, Thomas Rigel DC, who had practised in Italy for several years, chose to open Spain's first multi-disciplinary centre which was to emphasise chiropractic. It was located on the 16th floor of a Madrid high-rise, and since it was structured in such a way as to fall within the legal parameters of Spain, he was able to freely bring the doctrines of chiropractic to the general public. This was done through radio and television broadcasts and through written information which was published around the country. One of these publications was the booklet, *El Bienestar por la Quiropractica*. Two of the chiropractors who worked in the clinic were James Emch and Robert Burciaga, who would later become

two of the founding members the Spanish Chiropractic Association, *Asociación Española de Quiropráctica* (AEQ). At about the same time, Belgian chiropractor Robert Gevers opened his clinic in Madrid. These Madrid chiropractors, Emch, Burciaga and Gevers, would later initiate efforts to obtain legislation for the profession in Spain.

It became evident as years passed by that a professional association would be necessary to organise and promote chiropractic in Spain. In November of 1986, Robert Gevers, James Emch, Robert Burciaga, Antolin Silva and Christopher Hadley, with the assistance of lawyer Angel De Benito, founded the Spanish Chiropractic Association, which became a voting member of the ECU in December of that same year. Over the last 20 years, the membership of the AEQ has risen considerably, from 27 members in 1993 to 140 in October 2006.

The 1990s brought both pain and pleasure for the profession. It was during this time that the AEQ was granted scholarships by some American chiropractic colleges, which were to be offered to Spanish born citizens who wished to become chiropractors. Approximately 15 Spaniards were granted scholarships and returned to Spain upon graduation. In 1992 Spain hosted the annual ECU convention in Marbella, and in 1993 Spanish citizens Duque, Maguregui, de la Puente, Rasskin, and Suarez formed Spain's first Pro-Chiropractic Patients' Association. 1994 saw the publication of the AEQ sponsored book *La Profession*

Quiropractica, Bases cientificas y descripcion, by AEQ member Antolin Silva Couto. Its purpose was to educate members of other healthcare professions and influence decision makers within government. Unfortunately these positive developments for chiropractic were concomitant with legislated health professions filing the first legal complaints against chiropractors. Many cases were fought and settled in the courts.

In order to rectify the precarious legal position in which chiropractors find themselves in Spain, AEQ Executive Board members, led by past AEQ Presidents Robert Gevers, Juan Elizalde, Ricardo Puig, and current President Belén Sunyer, have had countless meetings at the Ministries of Health and Education in an attempt to obtain legal acceptance for chiropractic in Spain. They have also met with numerous university presidents in attempts to create an appropriate university-based degree in chiropractic, based on its existence as an autonomous and separate discipline, with its own identity and independence from other recognised healthcare professions. A critical step in achieving full and specific legalisation of the profession is the creation of a chiropractic

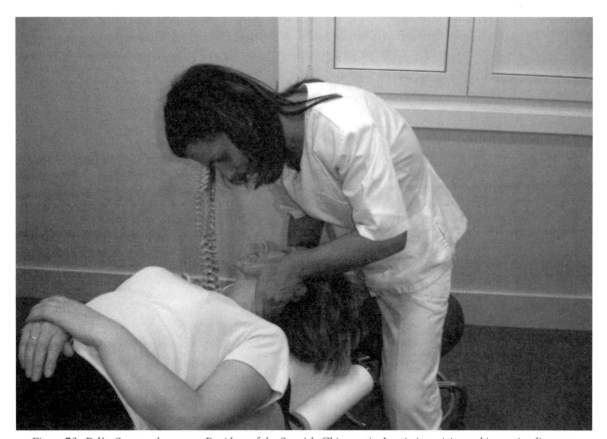

Figure 73. Belén Sunyer, the current President of the Spanish Chiropractic Association, giving a chiropractic adjustment

educational programme within Spain leading to recognition of a chiropractic qualification by the Registry of Official University Degrees.

In 1936, Pedro Alborna Soler wrote a letter to the President of the ECU, Dr Bannister. He said:

> "...after ten years of leaving me alone, [they] made me take the word "CHIROPRACTOR" off my door and cards, as they say it is not a Spanish Diploma. So I took it off."
>
> (*European Chiropractic Bulletin* 1936; 5 (2), 11)

Over 70 years have passed since that letter was sent. Chiropractic remains neither legal nor illegal in Spain. Spanish citizens who wish to study chiropractic still have to travel abroad to undertake their education. There are,

however, some very promising signs. Recently, talks have been underway with the Real Centre Maria Christina University near the Spanish capital of Madrid, with the intention of establishing a chiropractic undergraduate education in Spain. If all goes as planned, Spain's first chiropractic students will begin their studies in October of 2007. Within a few years we may see the first chiropractic graduates from a Spanish university entering the field.

Reference

† Spencer FW. La quiropráctica en España. In: *Quiropráctica: Formación, ejercicio, investigación y futuro de una profesión sanitaria.* Chapman-Smith DA. West Des Moines: NCMIG Group Inc.; 2004, pp. 5-17.

18. CHIROPRACTIC IN SWEDEN

A short history of chiropractic in Sweden, by Bengt Axén and Ann Hagéus

---

KEY FACTS: SWEDEN
Population: 9 million
National Chiropractic Association: Legitimerade Kiropraktorers Riksorganisation
Number of chiropractors registered with National Association (October 2006): 163
President of National Association (October 2006): Stina Berg
Website: www.kiropraktik.se

Simon B Lundin was the very first chiropractor in Sweden. He came in contact with chiropractic after he moved to the United States to work as a trained physiotherapist and masseur. There he came to witness what chiropractic could do for the patients he could

not help. He became so fascinated that he himself became a student at National College of Chiropractic, from which he later graduated. In 1921, he returned to Sweden to visit and treat friends and relatives. His skills were greatly appreciated, so he decided to stay

Figure 74. Simon B Lundin, the first chiropractor to practise in Sweden

of Chiropractic, he, like Lundin, came to Sweden in 1921. He set up practice in Malmö, in the very southern part of the country.

Other Swedish chiropractic pioneers were Frank Tollén, Jonas Berg, Thor Holmström, Martin Höije, Hjalmar Olofsson, and Carl Pettersson, who established their practices during the years of 1923 and 1924. Initially it would appear that these men were not aware of each other's existence, having set up in different parts of Sweden, however, following the critical articles in the press about chiropractic, they made contact with each other and decided to work together towards greater acceptance of chiropractic in Sweden. This eventually led to the formation of *Diplomerade Chiropraktorers Förening* in 1936, the forerunner of the Swedish Chiropractic Association (SCA). The Association started out with only 7 members. The initial purposes of the Association were to publish a journal about chiropractic, to work towards legislation for chiropractic in Sweden, and to preserve chiropractic principles. The first issue of *Kiropraktisk Journal* was published in 1936. Its purpose was to inform the public about chiropractic, its philosophy and history. It also commented on the negative accusations about chiropractors made in the press and provided testimonials from successfully treated patients.

and set up a practice in Nässjö, a town in the southern part of Sweden. Soon afterwards, negative articles about chiropractic started to appear in newspapers. On the 27th April 1924, there was an article in the national newspaper, *Dagens Nyheter*, with the headline "Quackery is growing. The laws are flaccid". The article was about a chiropractor who treated deaf and blind people.

Another early Swedish chiropractor was Lennart Thomson. Living in the United States, he suffered from arthritis which was helped by chiropractic treatment. As a consequence, he decided to train as a chiropractor. After receiving his diploma from National College

Another organisation founded in 1936 was a patients' organisation, formed in Helsingborg, in order to defend chiropractic principles, give moral support to chiropractic practitioners, and work towards legislation for chiropractic in

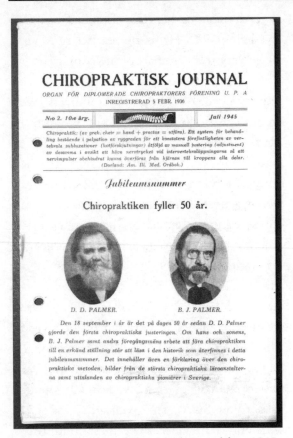

Figure 75. An issue of Kiropraktisk Journal from 1945,
organ of Diplomerade Chiropraktorers Förening

Sweden. Its Chairman was a very charismatic preacher, Martin Liljeblad, who had found chiropractic of great benefit for his asthma.

In 1938, Martin Höije, the Chairman of the Diplomerade Kiropraktorers Förening, had the opportunity to meet the King of Sweden, Gustav V. Martin Höije brought 2 patients with him, one who had been lame and the other deaf. Both, it was claimed, had been cured with chiropractic. He asked the King for an unbiased investigation to see whether chiropractic was quackery or not. The King, who in reality had little political power, could not assist, but thought the idea of an investigation was fair. Swedish chiropractors argued that chiropractic should be investigated as a possible treatment for different rheumatic diseases and for polio, and recommended that a specific chiropractic ward should be opened at a hospital which specialised in infectious diseases. Patients who did not improve with conventional care should also be allowed to try chiropractic treatment.

X-rays have been, and remain, an important diagnostic tool for chiropractors. Until 1941 there was no legislation in Sweden which prohibited chiropractors from owning or operating their own x-ray equipment. In 1941, however, the National Board of Health and Welfare decided that everyone who used x-ray equipment had to apply for a special permit. In 1944, all the chiropractors who had applied were denied a permit since the National Board of Health and Welfare could not determine their level of competence.

In the following years several unsuccessful attempts were made by Members of Parliament to pass bills regulating chiropractic. Over time the attitude of the primary antagonists towards chiropractic, the medical profession and the National Board of Health and Welfare, slowly changed. From accusing chiropractors of being quacks and unscientific, there was gradual acceptance that chiropractic had some benefit in regard to functional disorders of the mid and low back. The suggestion was then to include chiropractors among physiotherapists. That particular suggestion was rejected by the Swedish chiropractors.

By the 1980s chiropractors in Sweden had become such a strong and influential group that the medical profession realised that it was a lost cause to try and stop its development. In 1987, the Committee of Alternative Medicine suggested that chiropractors with a qualification of "Doctor of Chiropractic" should be authorised to practise under law. A new law came into effect in the summer of 1989. This law has enabled chiropractic patients to get some reimbursement from the government for fees, but it prohibits chiropractors from using spinal manipulative therapy (SMT) on children between the ages of 8 and 16 without medical referral. Children under the age of 8 are not allowed to be treated with SMT at all.

Today there are more than 150 chiropractors in Sweden with a Doctor of Chiropractic qualification from a college recognised by the European Council on Chiropractic Education (ECCE), but their field of practice is being challenged by large numbers of individuals describing themselves as naprapaths/chiropractors, trained in Sweden at 2 schools not recognised by the ECCE. The quality of education provided by these Swedish schools of manual therapy has been criticised by the National Agency of Higher Education. A recent report concluded that "neither of the courses met any of the requirements that the Agency applies to university education". The report also stated that in their current state, the schools do not produce naprapaths/chiropractors capable of providing competent healthcare.

Some of the future challenges for the SCA are to establish an internationally accredited chiropractic education in association with a university in Sweden, as well as to remove the constraint on treating children under the age of 16 with SMT. Further, the SCA would like to more effectively integrate chiropractic into the national healthcare system of Sweden. Today about 75% of the members of the SCA have limited funding from the county in which they practise, which subsidises patient fees.

19. CHIROPRACTIC IN SWITZERLAND

A short history of chiropractic in Switzerland, by Daniel Mühlemann and John P Naef

KEY FACTS: SWITZERLAND
Population: 7 million
National Chiropractic Association: Schweizerische Chiropraktoren-Gesellschaft
Number of chiropractors registered with National Association (October 2006): 246
President of National Association (October 2006): Franz Schmid
Website: www.chirosuise.info

Chiropractic had an exceptional beginning in Switzerland in that two women were the pioneers of the profession. Very little is known about the first, Hermine Fagan-Linder, which is probably not surprising given that she is thought to have practised secretly in a village close to Interlaken in the Bernese Oberland for a period of only about 6 years, between about 1919 until 1925. The second, Ida Gerber, a graduate of Eastern College of Chiropractic, New York, practised in Berne from 1927 onwards. In the same year the brothers Simon and Theo Müller took up practice in the Canton of Lucerne, and others followed.

In the early years, chiropractors were heavily prosecuted in Switzerland, as they were in a number of other European countries. High fines, closure of offices, and prison sentences were the potential consequences for those found guilty of the unauthorised practise of medicine. In response to the environment in which they found themselves, chiropractors united to form a professional organisation, and patients also rallied in their support. The Swiss Federation of Chiropractors was formed on 16th October 1932, with the first members being Fred Illi, Eduard Kropf, Simon Müller, Theo Müller, Emil Sigrist and Charles Regli. Regli had been instrumental in organising a meeting in London in 1931 to discuss the formation of a pan-European chiropractic organisation. Following those discussions, the European Chiropractic Union had come into existence.

As the number of patients seeking chiropractic care grew, so the government and the courts sought to better understand the discipline. Two reports in 1937 by members of the medical faculties of the Universities of Berne and Zürich, commissioned by court and government, concluded that chiropractic was an unreliable method of treatment and should be prohibited by law. Nevertheless, the health law of the Canton of Lucerne accepted chiropractic as an independent method of healing in 1937, and the Canton of Zürich followed suit in 1939 after a hard fought campaign and a public vote. These were the first laws to be passed in Europe which gave chiropractic specific statutory recognition.

By 1963, 15 of the 25 cantons of Switzerland,

covering 70% of the population, had established legislation for chiropractic. At that time, there were plans for a revision of the Federal Law on Health and Accident Insurance, which dated from 1911. Both chiropractors and the secular pro-chiropractic associations of the Swiss cantons lobbied for the inclusion of chiropractic services under the coverage of the new law. Heinrich Buchbinder, political advisor to the Swiss Federation of Chiropractors (and later to the ECU) had been instrumental in the formation of a united Swiss Pro-Chiropractic Association in the 1950s. This patient organisation launched a petition that collected almost 400,000 signatures from Swiss citizens who wanted chiropractic included in the new federal law. Through a process of political manoeuvring, chiropractors successfully circumvented attempts to have their practice included on the basis of medical referral only. The final votes of March 1964 in the 2 houses of parliament in Switzerland, the National Council and the Council of States, unanimously supported the inclusion of a chiropractic article in the insurance law. According to the law, persons who had obtained through special training a certificate of competence recognised by the Federal Council, and to whom a canton had granted a license for the practice of chiropractic, were entitled to practise independently within the scope of health insurance.

Following revision of the Law on Health and Accident Insurance in 1964, chiropractic services have been covered by mandatory

Figure 76. Ida Gerber, a chiropractor who practised in Berne from 1927

social insurances in cases of sickness and accident. Military and disability insurances introduced coverage for chiropractic in the years that followed. For more than 40 years chiropractors have been entitled to diagnose and treat patients in Switzerland, and have gradually obtained privileges similar to medical doctors. They have been able to prescribe sick leave and revisions of the law have widened chiropractic coverage to include such things as laboratory analyses, diagnostic imaging and medication.

Since the 1930s, legalisation has necessitated

entering into practice on their own.

The Association of Swiss Chiropractors, as the national association of chiropractors is now known, has recognised the need for continuing professional development of practitioners for many years. In 1960 it introduced annual postgraduate courses, the proceedings of which were published in the *Annals of the Swiss Chiropractors' Association* from 1960 to 1989. These courses are still mandatory for the Association's members and are also required by social insurers. The Association also introduced preparatory courses first for the cantonal exams, later for the inter-cantonal exams. This led to the establishment of the Swiss Chiropractic Institute in 1985.

Figure 77. Vote for chiropractic in Zürich! Posters in support of chiropractic, 1939.

Since 1995 a revision of the federal law on medical professions dating from 1877 has been in progress and is to be enacted in 2007. Chiropractic is to be included in this legislation, together, and on a par with medicine, dentistry, veterinary medicine, and pharmaceutics. The law is a further milestone in the development of chiropractic in Switzerland. There will be new rights and privileges for chiropractors, as well as new duties and responsibilities that will challenge the chiropractic profession as it matures in this century. Also, the University of Zürich, together with the Swiss Chiropractic Association, is in the process of establishing undergraduate chiropractic education in Switzerland.

rules and regulations for the practice of chiropractic in Switzerland. Cantonal laws required that chiropractors be competent and safe practitioners. This led to the formation of cantonal examining commissions. The federal law of 1964 led to the formation of an inter-cantonal examining commission following the example of the cantonal commissions. Today chiropractors wishing to practise in Switzerland are also required to undertake a two year assistantship programme before

INDEX